LATHE ACCESSORIES

Model and Allied Publications
Argus Books Limited,
14 St James Road, Watford, Hertfordshire, England

First Published 1943
Second Impression 1946
Third Impression 1947
Fourth Impression 1948
Fifth Impression 1951
Sixth Impression 1955
Seventh Impression 1958
Second Edition 1964
Second Impression 1971
Third Impression 1972
Fourth Impression 1973
Fifth Impression 1975
Sixth Impression 1978
Seventh Impression 1981

ISBN 0 85344 100 6

Printed in Great Britain
by Unwin Brothers Limited
The Gresham Press, Old Woking, Surrey, England
A member of the Staples Printing Group

LATHE ACCESSORIES

*Practical instructions for making and using numer-
ous ingenious accessories for metal-turning lathes*

EDGAR T. WESTBURY

MODEL & ALLIED PUBLICATIONS
ARGUS BOOKS LTD
14 St James Road, Watford, Hertfordshire
England

CONTENTS

PREFACE TO REVISED EDITION (1964)

SINCE the last revision of this handbook, many detail improvements have been made in small lathes and their accessory equipment. Although the basic principles of machine tools do not change, their efficiency is improved by modifications in design, and the application of better cutting tools and devices to extend the scope of operations. Most of the appliances described in the earlier editions of this book are still as useful as ever, but wherever possible they have been improved and brought into line with up-to-date practice, and many new items of equipment have been added.

Even the smallest workshops are now equipped much better than they were when this book was first written, and neither amateur nor professional engineers are content to make do with the primitive lathes, tools and devices which were once tolerated. Many useful lathe accessories are now available on the market, and where financial resources allow, most users will prefer to purchase them rather than take the trouble and time to make them; but there are many jobs where a simple home-made accessory will serve just as well as an elaborate and expensive one. Some of the appliances described in this book can be used to carry out operations for which no ready made equipment is available, and all can be made by a competent lathe user, from material which is available in the workshop, or easy to obtain.

Although, in a few cases, the devices may bear some resemblance to commercially-made articles, nearly all of them have some original features, and pains have been taken to avoid copying of proprietary designs covered by patents or registered trade marks. The object of the book is not to encourage the turner to produce makeshift substitutes for proper equipment, but to help him make the best use of available resources, and to solve in a practical manner the many problems which arise in general workshop practice.

Even in the most modern and well-equipped workshops, the use of simple additional machine tool accessories is not to be despised, and they may help to speed up production and improve general efficiency. Though specialised machine tools may be available to carry out operations beyond the normal scope of the lathe, it is often uneconomic to set them up for small jobs to which the lathe can readily be adapted. This applies to work such as circular or linear dividing, keyway cutting and certain kinds of milling, all of which can be carried out while the workpiece is set up for turning operations, and the risk of inaccuracy in a second set-up therefore avoided.

Some of the older accessories, dating from the days when turners were obliged to make all their special tools, have become extinct in modern industrial practice, but the individual worker will find them well worth keeping in mind. There is in fact a wide demand for information on making such items as cutters and D-bits, and this subject has been given special attention, though the use of these tools is not confined to lathe work. Other additional matter includes a description of knurling tools and their use, improved facilities for accurate indexing of the lathe mandrel, and simply-made running centres.

Several appliances have been based on ideas taken from articles published in the *Model Engineer* at various times, and due acknowledgments are made to the many contributors of these articles. For the rest, practical experience in carrying out a wide variety of machining work with very limited equipment has been applied to the selection of many well-tried devices, and the design of new ones, to assist and facilitate lathe work.

CHAPTER I

DEVICES FOR CENTRING WORK

OF the various methods of mounting work for turning in the lathe, one of the most popular and facile is by placing it between centres. Indeed, in the early types of lathes it was practically the only possible method of procedure, and, though in modern practice the improvements and increased application of chucking appliances has enabled them to be used for an ever wider range of operations, the use of the centres is by no means obsolete.

Little comment is needed on the centres themselves, as they form essential items of standard equipment on all modern engine lathes, and can be obtained ready made in all types and sizes. In the great majority of cases, they are made to fit tapered sockets in the headstock mandrel and tailstock barrel, and are interchangeable to fit in either position. The point centres, which are most commonly used, consist simply of a tapered shank with a conical point, which is almost universally made to a standard angle of 60 deg. inclusive. In the older lathes, the equipment also invariably included a square or " cutting " centre for the purpose of centring shafts, but this has now been almost entirely superseded by the modern centre-drill, though it is still useful on certain occasions. Other useful forms of centres are the large conical pipe centre, which is nowadays often made with a ball or roller bearing, to reduce running friction, the cutaway or " half " centre, which allows access for machining the end-faces of shafts, and hollow or " female" centres for dealing with shafts or pivots having pointed extremities. A lathe cannot really be considered well equipped unless it has one pair each of point and hollow centres, and one each at least of the others mentioned ; and in order to carry out accurate work, it is most essential that all centres fit their sockets properly, run dead truly, and have smoothly finished running surfaces.

In the original application of turning methods, the work was run between " dead " centres ; that is to say, both centres were stationary and non-rotative, the work being rotated by means of a pulley formed in it or directly attached thereto. This method is scarcely practicable in modern lathes, and has been superseded in favour of using a " live " or rotating centre in the mandrel socket. But it is worth noticing that the latter is, in some respects, a retrogression, because any concentric inaccuracy in the running of the live centre is transmitted to the work, whereas the use of dead centres at both ends ensures that positive concentricity of the work about its drilled or indented centres is always obtained. In some modern precision grinding machines, provision is made for running the work between dead centres, and the turner should never lose sight of the advantages of this principle in cases where the very utmost accuracy is necessary.

Methods of Centre-drilling

It is possible to mount work between centres with no more preliminary work than simply centre-punching the ends, but this is a very inefficient method. Not only may the indentations be inadequate in depth, so that there is a risk that they may fail to support the work under a heavy cut, but their roundness and conical angle may be inaccurate, so that they do not fit the lathe centres properly. The use of the square centre has already been referred to, but although this eliminates the above faults, it is a comparatively slow and tedious method of forming the centres, as the square centre is relatively inefficient as a cutting tool. It may, however, be quite efficiently used for *locating* the centre of work, which is afterwards drilled by other methods, or for correcting a drilled centre that is not truly concentric with the outside of the work.

A more efficient method of drilling the centres is by means of a short and stiff drill, having the tips ground so as to correspond exactly with the angle of the lathe centres. Such a drill may be made easily and quickly from a piece of round silver steel, with the end flattened by forging or filing, and the tips formed by holding it truly in the chuck and turning to the correct angle. After backing off the cutting edges, the drill is hardened and tempered, and care must be taken, in all subsequent grinding, to maintain the correct angle and concentricity of the point.

The most efficient tool for forming centres, however, is the modern " centre-drill," or, as it is often termed, the Slocombe drill, which is obtainable so cheaply nowadays that there is scarcely any excuse for any turner putting up with makeshift devices. Not only does this drill cut more efficiently than any improvised device ever can, and maintain the true angle in all circumstances, but the use of the small diameter pilot drill incorporated in it assists in finding the centre, and also provides a relief for the extreme tip of the lathe centre, preventing it from becoming overloaded. The only disadvantage of this tool is that it is relatively delicate, and easily broken by careless use, but no turner who claims to be a good craftsman should find any difficulty in getting long and efficient service from it.

Centre-drills and spear-point drills may both be used in a drill chuck, mounted in either the mandrel or tailstock socket, as occasion requires ; but it is better to mount them permanently in stub-holders, tapered to fit the socket, as this reduces the overhang of the drill from its point of support, and thus improves rigidity. (Fig. 1.)

When any of these devices are used to centre work running in the lathe chuck, it is most essential that they should be

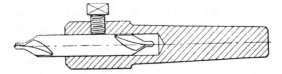

Fig. 1.—Centre-drill in holder to fit tailstock socket

presented exactly in alignment with the running axis. This requirement is automatically fulfilled in any good modern lathe, provided the tailstock is properly centred and the centre-drill chucked or socketed concentrically. But it

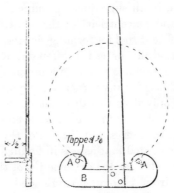

Fig. 2.—Centre square

cannot always be taken for granted in old or badly worn lathes, and in some cases it is necessary to compensate for misalignment of the tailstock by mounting the centre-drill eccentrically in its stub-holder. In such cases, care must always be taken to turn it into the correct position each time when inserting it in the socket.

Centre-finding devices

Whenever circumstances permit, it is advisable to centre shafts by mounting them in the lathe chuck and using a centre-drill in the tailstock socket. In the case of long shafts, in which the overhang causes a lack of rigidity at the outer end, some form of steady to support the latter may be found necessary. Often, however, it is impracticable

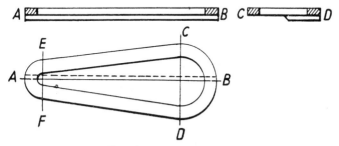

Fig. 3.—Centring device

to run the work in the lathe for centring, and it is necessary to carry out this operation by more primitive means.

The centre of a round or polygonal shaft may be found without a great deal of difficulty with the aid of a pair of " jenny " or odd-leg callipers, or by using a scribing block, but there are several devices obtainable, either ready-made, or made up by the turners themselves, for simplifying this operation. Of the former, the " mitre square," which forms a component of the combination rule sets made by several toolmaking firms, is deservedly popular ; but just as efficient results, on round work, can be obtained with the simple device shown in Fig. 2, which can be made easily and quickly from odd bits of sheet steel. Care is necessary in setting the locating pins and the riveted blade so that the latter bisects the angle of contact on round work of any diameter within the range of the device. Another very simple centre-finder, neither the construction nor use of which calls for explanation, is shown in Fig. 3.

Having used an appliance of the above type to scribe intersecting cross lines on the work, the centre thus found must be centre-punched, drilled and countersunk, either by hand or with such equipment as may be available. These operations leave many loopholes for errors, not the least of which is in the placing of the punch-dot relative to the intersection of cross lines. Some devices have therefore been designed to locate the punch central with the shaft

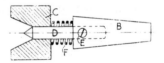

Fig. 4.—Centre drill with conical guide

without the necessity for first marking off cross lines. The simplest of these is the " bell centre punch," consisting of a hollow cone, extended at the small end to form a parallel guide for the centre punch. In use, the cone or " bell " is placed over the work, and centres the punch so that, when struck, it produces an indentation in the centre of the work. This tool used to be sold in almost every tool-shop, but for some reason is by no means so common nowadays. Although quite useful, it does not always produce quite the positive accuracy one might expect, as it is affected by lack of squareness of the end-face of the work, burrs on the edge of the work face, or by applying the bell out of axial alignment with it.

Centre drilling in the lathe

The principle of the bell centre punch may, however, be applied when centring work in the lathe, and enables work of any length within the capacity of the length of bed to be dealt with. This may be done by the simple device shown in Fig. 4, which consists of a stub-mounted spear-point or centre-drill, equipped with a spring-loaded internally conical guide. It will readily be understood that when the drill is fed up to the end of a slender unsupported shaft held in the lathe chuck, the cone first makes contact with the work

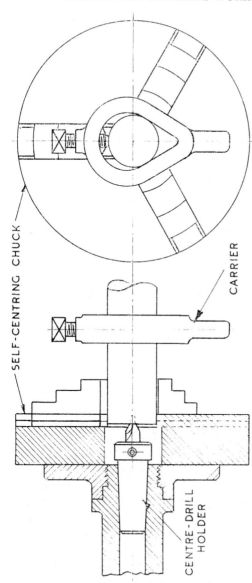

SELF-CENTRING CHUCK

CARRIER

CENTRE-DRILL HOLDER

Fig. 5.—Method of centre-drilling long bars, using the chuck jaws for location

and forms a running steady, thus ensuring that the drill enters truly in the centre. If desired, the device may be used in the live mandrel socket, the work in this case being rested in a similar internal cone fitted to the tailstock, and prevented from rotating by a lathe carrier clamped on it and held in the hand. As in the case of the bell centre punch, accuracy of centring is affected by roughness or lack of squareness of the work face, and these points should be attended to if the best results are to be obtained.

A still more accurate method of centring work from the live mandrel consists of using the jaws of the self-centring chuck as a steady. This method can hardly be recommended for extensive use, as it is liable to wear the chuck jaws unduly in the course of time, but if only used occasionally, and proper lubrication is applied, it will not be harmful. As shown in Fig. 5, it consists of using a stub-mounted centre-drill in the mandrel socket, sufficiently short to bring the tip of the drill well within the chuck jaws. The latter are closed *lightly* on to the work, so that they do not grip it, but just allow a fine working clearance. The other end of the work is rested on the tailstock centre, or in a conical guide as just described, and held against rotation by means of a carrier.

It should be noted that when using this method, slight inaccuracy of the chuck does not affect the concentricity of the centre drilled in the work but only results in the drill cutting slightly larger. In the case of a flat spear-point drill, however, it may possibly cause it to cut " out of round," and thus introduce a source of subsequent error.

Special devices have been made for centring the " live " end of the work while running in the chuck by means of a drill attached to a plunger working through the hollow mandrel, and something of this nature is not uncommonly applied to operations on automatic lathes. But the utility of such methods is by no means commensurate with their complication when applied to ordinary lathe practice.

Turning small rods between centres

Very small shafts or pivots present special difficulties to the turner with limited equipment, as they are too small to receive drilled centres, even if it were possible to locate them sufficiently accurately. In instrument or horological practice, these would be turned between hollow centres, the work first being held in a collet chuck and turned conical at each end. When this method is impracticable, the best way of mounting such work between centres is to fit temporary centring bushes to the ends, as shown in Fig. 6. These may be made from odd pieces of brass or steel rod held in the chuck, truly centred, drilled to fit tightly on the work, and parted off. They may, if desired, be sweated to the work to provide positive security, and in addition to ensuring true running of the work, they provide a much larger bearing surface than would otherwise be possible, and provide a suitable grip at each end for the carrier. In cases where clock or instrument pivots are turned by this method, extra length of stock must be allowed, to enable the pivots to be turned down between the centring bushes ; the ends are, of course, cut off after the turning operations are completed.

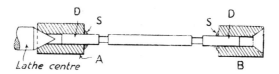

Fig. 6.—Turning small rods between centres

Alignment Testers

The correct alignment of the lathe centres is a most important factor in producing truly parallel work. Many turners keep a parallel test mandrel for the purpose of setting the tailstock centre in true alignment with that of the headstock, but unless a range of such mandrels, extending up to the maximum length accommodated by the lathe, is available, the application of this method is limited. The device shown in Fig. 7 is designed to be attached to the

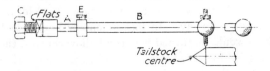

Fig. 7.—Testing alignment of tail centre

driver plate or face-plate, and being telescopic, is adjustable to suit a wide range of tailstock settings. In use, the pointer is set close up to the centre, and the lathe turned so as to bring it horizontally in line with the back and front of the centre in turn. The difference in the clearance at the two points can be gauged by eye, or preferably with the aid of feeler gauges, and the tailstock adjusted accordingly. If desired, it is possible to arrange for the mounting of a dial test indicator in place of the pointer, so as to provide the utmost accuracy in the application of the test.

When the tailstock is set for dealing with very short work, very small inaccuracies of alignment have more serious effects than when dealing with longer shafts. A very simple device for setting the centres in this case is shown in Fig. 8,

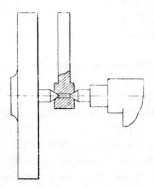

Fig. 8.—Device for setting centres

and consists of a bar with a cross-hole drilled right through and centred each end. The length of the bar, from the cross-hole, should be equal to the radius of the largest face-plate used on the lathe. It is used by putting it between centres and measuring by means of inside callipers from the outside end of the bar to the faceplate at various positions of rotation. Note that in applying this test, the lathe mandrel is held stationary and the bar rotated. By reversing this order, small inaccuracies in the concentric running of the live centre may be detected. As the radius of the bar is greater than the distance between the centres, any inaccuracy in alignment or true running is magnified, and thus more easily measured than would otherwise be possible.

Ball and roller bearing centres

When heavy cuts are taken at high speed on work running between centres, the friction on the tailstock centre is excessive, and rapid wear may take place either of the centre itself or the centred end of the work. To avoid this, the use of tailstock centres equipped with ball or roller bearings is becoming increasingly common, and such centres are now obtainable in all standard sizes.

A simple form of running centre, suitable for use on small lathes, is shown in Fig. 9. It comprises a shank turned to fit the taper socket of the tailstock, on which the loose head rotates freely, and end thrust is taken on a single steel ball. The parts must be carefully machined, and after the conical head has been rough turned and bored, it should be wrung on to a true-running plug mandrel to finish the outside truly concentric with the bore. All working surfaces should be case-hardened, and the inside of the head is packed with grease when in use. If closely fitted, as it should be, an air vent in the head will be found necessary to allow it to be pushed home on the shank. No means of retaining the head on the shank is shown, but it may be added if desired. By making the head readily removable, it is possible to provide spare heads, such as to serve for pipe centres, which can be fitted at a moment's notice. While this device is not so well suited to very heavy and continuous work as the standard type, it is much more compact, and is easily made in the home workshop.

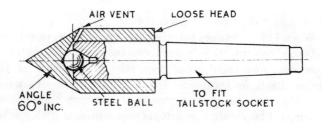

Fig. 9.—A simple form of running centre for the tailstock

CHAPTER II

CHUCKING ACCESSORIES

THE term " chuck," as used in lathe practice, may be applied to any fitting used to attach work rigidly to the lathe mandrel, so that it can be rotated about the mandrel axis. It thus covers a wide diversity of lathe accessories, some of them quite simple and others elaborate and complex. The ordinary lathe faceplate is virtually a form of chuck, though it is not usually defined as such ; but faceplate fixtures are considered as chucking accessories within the scope of this chapter.

Nearly all engineering lathes nowadays are equipped with one or more chucks of approved standard type as necessary fittings for dealing with general work. There are three main forms of these chucks ; namely, the " independent-jaw " chuck, the self-centring or " scroll " chuck, and the split collet chuck. Drill chucks of various types, though extensively used in connection with lathe work, are not generally used for holding the work, and therefore do not come within the present category.

It is not proposed to deal in detail with the standard forms of chucks, which are invariably obtained ready-made, and the use of which calls for no explanation here, as it forms an elementary part of turning practice which should be understood by every lathe operator. Some advice on the adaptation of chucks to suit special chucking problems may, however, be found helpful.

The independent-jaw chuck, which is usually made with four jaws, each controlled by an individual screw, is perhaps

the most useful and adaptable of all. It may be said to
have evolved from the old " dog chuck," which consisted
simply of an ordinary faceplate on which were mounted four
screw " dogs," enabling work to be gripped radially, in
addition to the usual facilities for clamping it sideways to
the plate. Although this form of
chuck is now practically obsolete,
and is certainly by no means as
handy as the modern independent-
jaw chuck, there are certain lathe
operations in which the combination
of radial and side grip is extremely
useful, or even indispensable, and
with which the standard chuck cannot deal effectively. Screw dogs

Fig. 10.—Screw dog for
lathe faceplate

of the type shown in Fig. 10, however, can be fitted to
practically any faceplate, so as to convert it into a primitive
form of " dog " chuck ; and it is sometimes possible
to arrange for clamping work to the face of a four-jaw
chuck, in addition to using the jaws. But few such
chucks, at least in small or moderate sizes, are provided
with slots in the bodies to take clamping bolts, and
it is scarcely advisable to drill holes indiscriminately
in a chuck, unless it is a spare one, which has already
served its legitimate span of normal use. In cases
where one or more of the chuck jaws is not occupied
in gripping the work, however, it is possible to utilise
the jaw slot for anchoring a clamping bolt, by removing
the jaw entirely and replacing it with a similar-shaped
tongue forming the head of the clamping bolt, or
tapped to receive it. This method must, however, be
used with discretion ; it is most important that the
tongue should be very carefully fitted to the slot, and that
it is not over-strained, or the chuck may be permanently
damaged. Examples of the utility of faceplate dogs are
given in Figs. 11 and 11a.

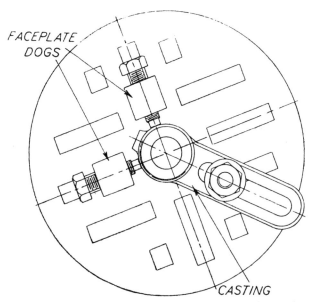

FACEPLATE
DOGS

CASTING

Fig. 11.—Use of faceplate dogs to centre boss of soleplate casting

Both independent and self-centring chucks may be adapted to form " chucking jigs " to deal with awkwardly shaped work, or to save time in setting up parts in repetition work. In the former type of chuck the method in most cases is to remove all the jaws but one, and to attach in their place a single block, or a number of blocks, so located and shaped as to fit the work-piece to be chucked, in its proper location to the lathe centre. The one remaining jaw is then used to clamp the work against the fixed block.

Self-centring chucks are often adapted for repetition work, by providing them with soft jaws, which are bored or otherwise machined out to the size and shape required, and when once initially set will hold the parts dead truly until their accuracy is destroyed by wear and tear. Generally, a special form of chuck is used, having seatings and

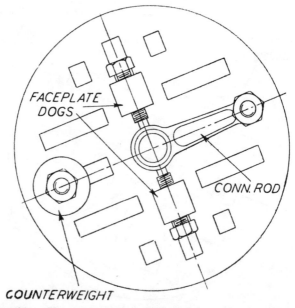

Fig. 11a.—Use of faceplate dogs to centre connecting rod
bearing eye

attachment screws on the main scroll jaws to take the soft
jaws ; but any old self-centring chuck can be adapted by
softening the jaws and either machining them as required,
or by cutting away the stepped portion and drilling and
tapping to take screws, by means of which mild steel jaws
can be attached. It is worthy of note that it does not
matter whether the chuck itself is accurate or not ; if the
jaws are machined *in situ* to the exact size of the work it is
desired to grip, it is bound to be held concentrically. The
large area of gripping surface formed in this way also provides a much firmer grip than can be obtained with the
usual form of jaws, without risk of damaging the work.

When parts have to be turned eccentrically to a previously
machined surface, such as in making certain types of crank-
shafts, this work may often be facilitated by mounting

either an independent or self-centring chuck eccentrically on the lathe faceplate. It is generally advisable to remove the adaptor or backplate, in this case, and clamp the body of the chuck directly to the plate, to reduce the overhang and promote rigidity. The utility of this method, when a number of parts have to be machined to accurate limits in respect of throw, will be obvious. Carrying this idea still further, the chuck may be mounted on an angle plate attached to the lathe faceplate, in order to machine parts at right angles to a previously turned shaft surface ; but in this case the weight and bulk of a full-sized lathe chuck would be a disadvantage, as it would be all unbalanced weight, and would have to be counter-balanced. A small chuck, thus mounted, might, however, be found very useful.

Home-made chucks

The old-time turner was often obliged to make his own chucks, and although some of these were of a very primitive type, they served their purpose, even on work of extreme accuracy. A very common form of chuck consisted of a piece of hardwood attached to the faceplate or the mandrel nose, and bored out to take the work, which was simply pressed in and held by friction. In some cases, the chucks were more elaborately made in boxwood or similar hard material, and occasionally fitted with screws, or split and externally screwed, to take a contracting nut by means of which they could be tightened up, or accommodated to work varying slightly in diameter.

The good old-fashioned " bell chuck " has now died a natural death, and few will mourn its passing, as it was an extremely difficult chuck to adjust properly, and often severely tried the temper of the operator. But even this primitive form of chuck had its merits, one of which was that it could be adjusted to hold work out of *angular* align-ment with the lathe axis, a feature not possessed by other types of chucks, and of dubious advantage in ordinary work, but **very** useful in certain unusual and awkward operations. A fixture very similar to a bell chuck is sometimes used as a holder for interchangeable bushes or jigs, to hold small components in production work. The jigs are sometimes made by casting a matrix of the component in soft metal, and turning it outside to fit the chuck, on a centre coinciding with that to be used for the turning operation.

Collet chucks

Very serviceable and accurate chucks to take standard or home-made split collets can be made on the lathe on which they are to be used. The simplest method of applying standard collets is to make an adaptor bush to fit the mandrel socket, and to bore it internally to the size and angle of the collet. This form of adaptor, however, will only take a small size collet—in the case of a mandrel socket of No. 1 Morse taper, the largest size standard collet which can be used is " A "

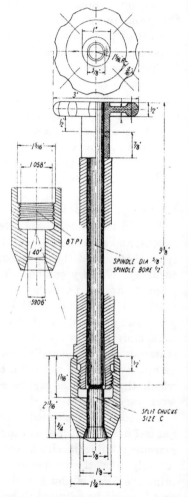

Fig. 12.—Details of split collet adaptor

size (8 mm.). In order to accommodate a larger collet, an adaptor may be made to screw on the mandrel nose, and provided it is carefully made, and bored out *in situ*, it will hold the collets, and thus the work, perfectly truly. Particulars of an adaptor of this type to take " C " size (15 mm.) collets on a 3-in. lathe, together with its draw-in spindle, are given in Figs. 12, 13, 14 and 15.

When standard split collets are not available, the chuck shown in Fig. 16 will be found very easy to adapt, as the collets can be made up very quickly as and when required, and do not need hardening. No draw-in spindle is used, so that it can be applied to lathes which are not bored right

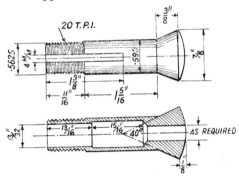

Fig. 13.—Standard split collet (size " C ")

through the mandrel. Although the overhang is greater than with the draw-in type of chuck, and there is, theoretically, greater possibility of error, practical experience with this chuck has proved that it will hold work true and rigid under the hardest conditions of use.

Faceplate fixtures

For mounting work on the faceplate, most turners keep a heterogeneous collection of bolts and flat bars of various lengths and sizes, and it is an axiom in the machine shop that however large and varied this collection, it rarely seems adequate to cope with all eventualities. But while it is clearly impossible to envisage a universally applicable form

Fig. 14.—The complete collet chuck in use

of clamping plate, there are some forms of these simple fittings which are handier or more useful than others, so that it is worth while to make a set of them specially, instead of relying entirely on odd pieces available, or made specially

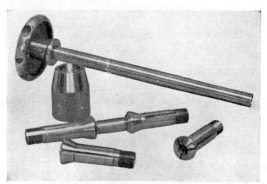

Fig. 15.—Parts of collet chuck, with finished and unfinished spare collets

for the job. It may be pointed out that, although it is common to refer to all fittings of this nature as " dogs," this is a very loose term, and it is proposed to call them

" clamps," to distinguish them from the " screw dogs " previously mentioned.

A very common form of clamp is that shown in Fig. 17, which is obtainable ready-made in various sizes, but is also easy enough to make by forging or cutting from the solid. The long slot gives it the widest possible range of adjustment relative to the faceplate slot, and the reduced width and depth of the extended finger enables it to be used close up to the machined surface with the minimum risk of fouling the tool.

The clamp shown in Fig. 18 is still easier to make, and the turned-down end enables the use of packing blocks to be dispensed with, but of course it is only applicable to a limited range of work thickness. This might be remedied by fitting a jack screw to the tail of the clamp instead of turning it down, and clamps thus equipped are not uncommon, but are less popular than the simple one-piece type. Adjustable packings, such as wedge blocks or bottle-jacks are quite useful in some classes of work, but in small lathe practice they are liable to be cumbersome and take up too much

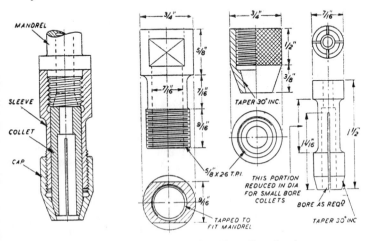

Fig. 16.—Simple form of split collet chuck

room, so that solid packings are more popular. It is nearly always better to use a single piece of packing of the required thickness, whenever possible, than to build up with two or three thinner slips. This makes a more rigid job, and, if

clamps have to be slackened while setting up the work, there is less likelihood that odd bits of packing will fall out of place, and thereby put undue strain on skill and patience in their manipulation. The angle plate is used almost universally when it is

Fig. 17.—Simple clamp

necessary to locate work at right angles to a true reference surface. Angle plates of all sizes and types are obtainable ready made, and are quite cheap, but occasions often arise where it is necessary to improvise an angle plate for some special purpose. A piece of common angle iron can be made into a serviceable angle plate by filing or machining its surfaces to a true right angle, and drilling bolt holes where required. This lacks the rigidity of a standard cast angle plate, but could, if the necessity should arise, be stiffened by brazing or welding struts to it. In some cases, a block of hardwood, planed truly square on two adjacent sides, can be used as an angle plate.

Fig. 19 shows an improvised fitting of this nature in use for boring a split plummer block. In this case the face-plate is also made of hardwood, attached to the lathe mandrel by means of a wood-turning screw chuck, and machined on the face while in position so that its truth is beyond suspicion.

Fig. 18.—Another simple form of clamp

The use of hardwood fittings in lathe work will often help to solve problems in chucking or otherwise securing work for machining, as the wood can be shaped to suit the par-

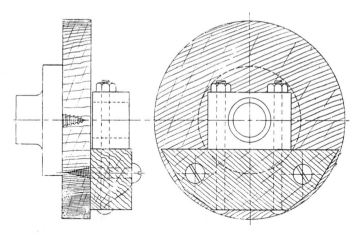

Fig. 19.—Improvised angle plate

ticular job much more easily than metal. Often, when a piece of work has to be turned at some odd but definite angle to a reference surface, the use of a fitting such as that

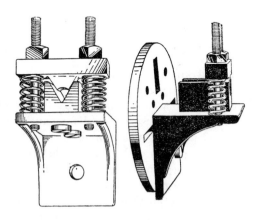

Fig. 20.—Improvised vee angle plate

just described, but with the work bolting face planed to the required angle, forms the simplest and most practical solution. Irregular shaped work is often best dealt with by bedding it into a piece of wood gouged out to the required contour.

Considerable discretion is called for in using wood in this

Fig. 21.—Another simple form of vee angle plate

way, because all kinds of wood are compressible to some extent, and the local pressure when the work is tightly clamped may cause it to be thrown badly out of truth. In repetition work, the use of wood for chucking fixtures would not be tolerated, though it might be used for packings which have nothing to do with positively locating the work. For machining one or two pieces, in which the expense of a metal fixture is not justified, wood is very useful if used with discretion. The most suitable hardwoods are those with a very close and homogeneous grain, such as beech, boxwood, lignum vitae, pearwood or mahogany.

Vee blocks of various kinds are very useful as accessories for faceplate chucking, either bolted directly to the faceplate or attached to an angle plate. The well-known Keats vee angle plate is the best-known example of a ready-made appliance of this nature, but long before its introduction, devices more or less equivalent in function were often improvised by turners to suit special problems in handling work. Fig. 20 shows an appliance of this nature that can

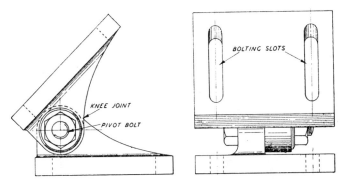

Fig. 22.—Adjustable angle plate

easily be fitted up and is extremely useful for dealing with many awkward chucking problems, including eccentric turning, and is also useful on the drilling machine, or for use as a pipe-vice on the fitting bench. Another very simple form of vee angle plate is shown in Fig. 21. An adjustable angle plate is an extremely useful accessory for attaching work either to the faceplate or the saddle of the lathe for operating on surfaces at odd angles. Devices of this nature are usually very elaborate and expensive, but the simple fitting shown in Fig. 22 may be made up either from castings or from two built-up pieces of mild steel, and will hold work quite securely at any angle.

Solder and cement chucks are not very extensively used in engineering practice nowadays, but they are useful for dealing with small jobs that are difficult to chuck by other

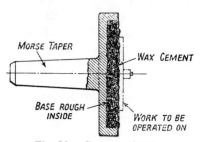

MORSE TAPER

WAX CEMENT

BASE ROUGH INSIDE

WORK TO BE OPERATED ON

Fig. 23.—Cement chuck

methods. They consist of small faceplates either fitted directly to the lathe mandrel or held in a chuck, and to which the work is temporarily attached by soft solder or by plastic cement, such as shellac, pitch, resin, or Chatterton's compound. The use of solder is, of course, preferable on the grounds of security, but while cement is only suitable for very light work, it has the advantage of remaining plastic for some time after the chuck has been warmed up and

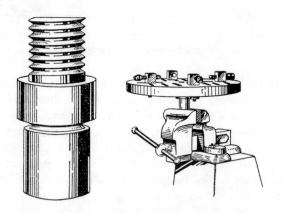

Fig. 24.—Chuck and faceplate holder

thus allowing the work to be shifted slightly for the purpose of setting up. The cement chuck shown in Fig. 23 has a cavity in the face, internally roughened to hold the cement.

Chuck and faceplate holders

In the preliminary setting up of work in a chuck, or on a faceplate (particularly the latter), it is often a great convenience to be able to lay the plate in a horizontal plane. This may be facilitated by turning up a short shaft, with the end screwed to the same size and pitch as the lathe mandrel nose, and fitting the chuck or faceplate to it temporarily. It may then be held in the vice as shown in Fig. 24, to provide the utmost facility in handling the work while being set up.

A further development of this idea is, instead of clamping the shaft directly in the vice, to fit it to a bush holder so that it is rotatable while in this position. If the bush is split, it may be clamped up on the shaft, to prevent it rotating, by tightening the vice up firmly. Another useful addition consists of boring the centre of the shaft to take a parallel rotatable spindle, extended above the plate and equipped to carry an adjustable scriber similar to that fitted to a surface gauge. This fitting will be found a great help in the concentric setting of bushes, etc., on the faceplate.

CHAPTER III

TOOL HOLDERS AND CUTTER BARS

ALTHOUGH all lathe tools may legitimately be classed as
" lathe accessories," it is not considered possible, within the
scope of this book, to describe in detail how all types of them
are made and used. Neither is it possible to describe the
innumerable types of tool holders, most of which embody
useful and ingenious features, either produced by turners
for their own use, or put on the market by enterprising
manufacturers at various times. Some notes on the basic
principles of tool holders for various purposes in external
and internal turning processes, and descriptions of simple
devices of this nature which can be made quite easily, will,
however, be found helpful to many amateur and professional
turners.

During recent years, the old practice of forging lathe tools
from solid steel has very largely been superseded in favour
of using small pieces of tool steel, attached in various ways
to shanks or holders, which may be made of any material
strong and rigid enough to withstand cutting stresses.
The advantages of this method are twofold ; first, the small
inserted cutters dispense with the need for forging, and, in
most cases, hardening and tempering as well, as they can be
cut off and ground to shape from heat-treated tool steel bar.
Secondly, they effect considerable economy in the use of
tool steel, a very important consideration when using the

best grades of modern high-speed steel, which are much more costly than the carbon steel formerly used for solid tools.

The usual method of attaching the small cutter to the

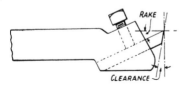

Fig. 25.—Tool mounted in holder at cutting angle

holder is by means of a clamping screw, which is certainly very quick and convenient, and enables the holder to be equipped with a range of interchangeable cutters of various shapes to suit different operations. So far as light work is considered, this method of holding the cutters is quite satisfactory, but in very heavy work the rigidity of the cutter is open to question, and it may possibly move under stress, or the clamping screw loosen by vibration; the conductivity of heat from the cutting edge to the shank is also inferior to that of a solid tool. The latest practice in lathe tools for production work, therefore, is to use a very small tip of tool steel or " cutting alloy," attached to a mild

steel shank by brazing or welding. Not only does this provide a measure of rigidity equal to that of a solid tool, but it also economises still further with special alloys, which may in many cases be classed as " precious metals " nowadays.

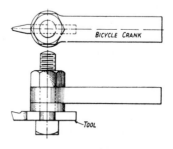

Fig. 26.—Simple tool holder

The simple form of toolholder having a clamped-in cutter is by no means obsolete yet, however, and users of light lathes will find that it answers most of their requirements quite satisfactorily. Of the many commercial types of tool holders for external work, the most popular is that which holds the tool at such an angle that a top rake sufficient for cutting steel or other metals is provided without the necessity of grinding the top face of the cutter (Fig. 25). In order to obtain the maximum life from the cutters, a constant and fairly fine clearance angle should be ground on the front face, and also on the side if necessary, and these faces only should be reground when the tool is sharpened.

The very simple tool holder shown in Fig. 26, which holds the cutter in horizontal position, and enables it to be swivelled round through a wide angle for front or side cutting, may

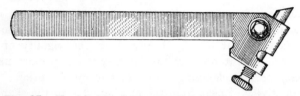

Fig. 27.—Tool holder incorporating height adjustment

be made from the small end of an old bicycle crank, cut off about 4 in. from the eye. The latter is fitted with a ½ in. bolt having a crosshole immediately behind the head to take either a round or square cutter, ¼ in. diameter. A thick washer is fitted above the tool to take the clamping pressure.

This form of tool has the advantage that the tool point is " dropped " below the point of support of the shank, so that if it is overloaded, it springs away from the work instead of digging in. As the shank must be mounted well above the level of the lathe centres, however, it may not be found suitable for use in some forms of light lathes which have limited room in the tool post.

The tool holder shown in Fig. 27, which is obtainable commercially in various sizes to suit lathes up to 6 in. centres, embodies some interesting features, not the least of which is the provision for accurate height adjustment of the cutter bit, which is made from a short length of round tool-steel ground off on the end to provide the required angle of rake. By using the steel in this way, a smoothly rounded nose is provided which is extremely useful for turning fillets, as its radius is definitely known and always constant, and it is also useful for fine finishing of steel parts.

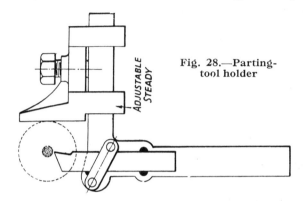

Fig. 28.—Parting-tool holder

ADJUSTABLE STEADY

The excellent chip-clearing properties of tools made on this principle also render them suitable for quite heavy work, so long as suitable steel is used for the cutters.

Many forms of tool holders have been devised to take parting cutters, which, by reason of their narrowness and lack of side rigidity, are by no means easy to clamp securely. One of the most satisfactory parting-tool holders ever produced commercially was that made by Burnerd, which incorporated a special steadying device, by means of which the prevalent tendency to dig in, nearly always experienced with any form of parting tool, could be entirely prevented. So far as can be ascertained, this tool is not at present on the market. A tool holder which incorporates similar features, however, and is simple to make, is shown in Fig. 28. It is designed to take tool steel of tapered section, as supplied for parting cutters, but at a pinch it is possible to use a piece of high-speed machine hacksaw blade. The adjustable steady may be made from the sliding jaw of an old shifting spanner, which should be trued and smoothed up on the working face, and case hardened. The stock may be built up by brazing or welding, and the blade is located by steady pins, and clamped by the narrow steel strap, which is fitted with screws at either end.

Spring tools for producing a high finish on turned work are not so popular as they used to be, mainly because the lathe has largely been superseded, as a finishing machine, by the cylindrical grinder in modern production practice. Often, however, grinding facilities are not available, or are inapplicable—as when work has to be formed to a special profile—when a spring tool may be found very useful. Instead of the orthodox form of forged swan-neck spring tool, a spring holder fitted with a detachable cutter will be found simpler to make and much more adaptable. The holder shown in Fig. 29 may be made from mild steel, and the cutter, which may be made from a piece of gauge steel, machine hacksaw blade, or a broken file, is attached by a box clamp. Form cutters of any desired profile may be filed to shape before hardening, and subsequently should

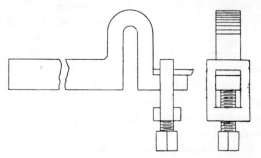

Fig. 29.—Spring tool holder

be sharpened by grinding the top surface only ; an example of a suitable form of tool bit is shown in Fig. 30.

The above type of tool is not intended to be used for heavy work, as its particular advantages apply only when it is used for light finishing cuts. For heavy forming, a rigid tool is recommended, but the ordinary straight forming tool, even if made fairly deep, tends to have a comparatively short life, because of the continual regrinding of the top face necessary from time to time. Much longer wear can be obtained by making the cutter in the form of a disc, which is turned to the required profile and, after hardening and tempering, attached to the shank by means of a pivot bolt which enables it to be turned round as required (Fig. 31). The cutting edge

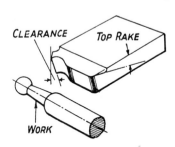

Fig. 30.—Tool bit for form cutter

is formed by grinding a notch in the edge of the disc, and it will readily be seen that the grinding of the cutting face may be continued until nearly the whole of the circumference of the disc has been used up. This principle is also applicable to screwcutting tools for cutting accurate thread forms, to machine chasers, and, in certain cases, to parting tools.

Cutters of this type may be clamped by the pivot bolt to the side of a plain rectangular bar, but are much more securely held if the end of the bar is forked, so that the cutter is gripped on both sides. It is also an advantage to provide large and even surface areas on both cutter and holder to

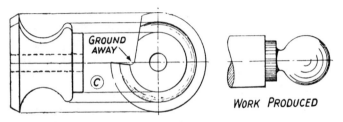

Fig. 31.—Disc form of cutter, giving longer life

ensure an efficient friction grip. Even so, there may be a
tendency for the cutter to turn on its pivot when dealing
with heavy work, and some positive means of preventing this
may be necessary. The simplest method of doing so is to
make a second notch in the cutter, diametrically opposite
to the original cutting edge, and to arrange a fixed or
adjustable abutment on the holder to engage this notch. If
the latter is made identical in shape with the first, it forms a
second auxiliary cutting edge, which should be used alter-
nately, so that both notches are ground away equally, and
preserve their true opposite location. This will ensure that
the cutting edge in use is kept at the correct height, relative
to the lathe centres, when the tool is in use.

Boring tools

In tools for interior turning, or " boring," the use of
inserted cutters is often more than merely convenient or

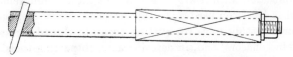

Fig. 32.—Simply made boring tool

economical—it may be absolutely necessary. Many operations call for a specially-shaped tool at a moment's notice,
and the only practicable method of satisfying this requirement is to grind up a small cutter and attach it to a tool
holder or " boring bar." As in the case of external tool
holders, there are innumerable forms of these devices, many
of them obtainable ready-made ; all have their points. A
very simple form of boring tool holder, which may be very
quickly made and holds the cutter very securely, is shown in
Fig. 32. It is made from a piece of square section mild steel of
suitable size to clamp in the lathe tool post, faced truly on the
ends and drilled right through from end to end with a drill

about half its diameter ; a piece of thick steel tube having a bore the same size as the latter ; and a length of mild steel round bar to fit this bore, long enough to pass through both pieces and screwed at the end to take a Whitworth or B.S.F. nut. No attempt is made to give exact dimensions, as they must obviously vary with the size of lathe on which the tool is used and also the nature of the work to be undertaken.

The cutter may be of either round or square section, and is fitted to a cross hole which passes through the end of the tube and the internal rod. For dealing with through holes, this may be drilled squarely across, but when it is necessary for the tool to reach the end of a blind hole it must be fitted at an angle, as shown. The special merit of this form of tool is that it avoids the necessity for fitting the inner

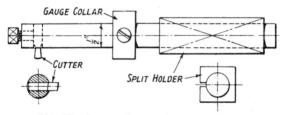

Fig. 33.—Internal recessing tool fitted to plain bar

end of the bar with a set screw. A set screw, if large enough to hold the cutter really firmly, is almost certain to occupy space that can ill be spared.

Variations of this form of tool include the use of a single-piece shank, consisting of a long square bar turned down cylindrically for half its length or more. This is more rigid, but entails a long endwise hole that may possibly be tedious to drill. Alternatively the shank may be made from a long piece of tube, held in a split square holder or a vee packing strip.

The use of a split holder, either for inserted cutter bars or solid round-section tools, is deservedly popular among turners, as it will hold any tool having the correct size of. shank instantly and securely. Fig. 33 shows an internal recessing tool fitted to a plain bar, which is held in such a

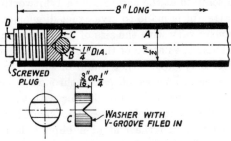

Fig. 34.—Making tubular boring bar

holder, and also illustrates a very simple method of measuring endwise distances when turning internal grooves or recesses. It consists of a gauge collar, adjustable along the bar, and set by measurement from the cutter, either by means of a rule or a pair of inside callipers. When the bar is fed into the hole until the collar touches the face of the work, the cutter has definitely reached the set depth. Care must be taken when using this device that measurements are not affected by swarf getting between the face of the work and the collar.

A simple method of making a tubular boring bar is shown in Fig. 34, in which it will be seen that the end of the tube is tapped to take an ordinary gas plug, which bears on the end of a vee-notched pad, and thus secures the cutter firmly

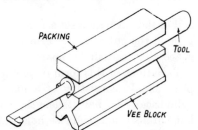

Fig. 35.—Use of vee packing block

in the cross hole. This method can be adapted to hold the cutter at an angle, if desired, or to hold square or flat cutters by shaping the end of the pad to suit.

Vee packing blocks are very useful to hold small boring tools for delicate operations, and Fig. 35 shows how a block of this type is used. It will be seen that vee-grooves are cut in all four sides, of varying depths so as to provide height adjustment. The method of milling the vee-grooves in the lathe with the aid of a flat counterskinking bit or rosebit is also shown. These vee packing blocks will be found useful for innumerable purposes on the lathe and other machine tools.

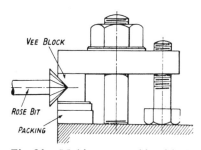

Fig. 36.—Making vee packing block

They may be made very simply by holding a piece of square bar in the tool post, and milling a vee groove along it by means of a flat countersink or rosebit held in the lathe chuck (Fig. 36). If this type of cutter does not work very efficiently in its capacity as a milling cutter, the operation may be expedited by relieving the centre with a slitting saw, and roughing the slot out to a part of its depth with a small end mill or slot drill, before using the countersink. It will be noted that the boring tool used in Fig. 35 is of

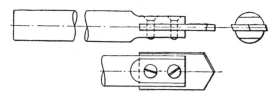

Fig. 37.—Example of flat drill

a type which can be turned very simply from round tool steel bar. Instead of shaping the end as shown, it can be made on the principle of the disc forming tool previously described, a notch being ground in the formed portion to act as the cutting edge; in this way the life of the tool will be greatly increased.

Flat drills for rough-boring or sizing holes may be made with inserted cutters, thus saving a good deal of work in producing a drill of a given size, besides saving tool steel. A single holder, which may be made with a round or square shank for tool post mounting, or equipped with a Morse taper to fit the tailstock socket, can be used to hold cutter bits of any size. Fig. 37 shows a drill of this type, and similar methods may be used for holding counterboring or end-forming cutters of any kind.

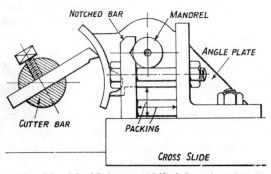

Fig. 38.—Machining a saddle joint of engine cylinder

Cutter bars for saddle boring

The use of cutter bars rotating either between centres or attached in some way to the lathe mandrel, for boring work clamped to the saddle or carriage of the lathe, is to be recommended when dealing with heavy castings that present difficulties in chucking, or are outside the normal capacity of the lathe. Such bars are often made in a hurry from any odd piece of shafting, and without any very great care in true centring, but while they are quite satisfactory when considered purely as cutter holders, the use of a true-running and parallel bar is of great assistance while setting up, as radial measurements may be taken directly from it. Thus the distance of the rough bore of the work, measured by internal callipers from the bar at both ends, and at all points of rotation, may be taken as a check on concentric setting. A bar of definite diameter also enables the radial projection of the cutter to be set readily for cutting to an exact diametral measurement by means of a depth gauge.

Segmental machining of work faces to a definite radius, such as saddle pieces to fit on cylindrical surfaces, may readily be carried out by the above methods, and it is also possible to machine external surfaces to a limited extent by using bent cutters in the bar.   Fig. 38 shows how the saddle

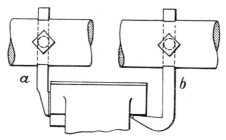

Fig. 39.—Tools for end-facing and turning
lip of saddle shown in Fig. 38

joint of a traction engine cylinder may be machined to fit the boiler barrel, and the tools for end-facing the saddle and turning its external lip are shown in Fig. 39.

The cutters may be secured in rotating boring bars by methods similar to those applied to stationary bars, but there are many occasions when the ordinary set screw takes up too much room, and it is impracticable to use endwise screws owing to the ends of the bar being centred.   In early lathe practice, cutters were often secured by cotters or wedges, and this method is well worth considering where space is limited. A very simple fixing of this nature is shown in Fig. 40, and consists of a taper pin fitted to the shaft at right angles to the cutter. The taper hole slightly cuts into the hole for the cutter, and the pin may, if desired, be flattened on this side to form a wedge, but in many cases it will be better to notch the cutter, so that it is positively located by the pin. This is particularly useful in the case of double - ended "sizing" cutters like that shown, which obviously must project an exactly equal distance each side of the bar.

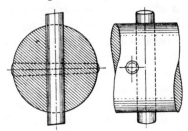

Fig. 40.—Cotter method of securing cutters to shaft

Double - ended cutters are often required to be made adjustable to suit slight variations of bore size or to compensate for grinding the cutting edges. Various elaborate methods of adjusting the cutters are often used in special forms

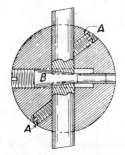

Fig. 41.—Self-centring method of adjusting cutters in boring bar

of cutter bars, but the method shown in Fig. 41 is very simply applied to any bar, and is perfectly self-centring. The cutter is originally made in one piece, and has a cross hole drilled and taper-reamered to fit the tapered adjusting screw B. After the edges have been ground or otherwise shaped, so as to project equally either side of the bar, the cutter is sawn across through the taper hole, when the two halves can be adjusted radially by turning the adjusting screw B, and individually locked by the two grub screws AA.

CHAPTER IV

DIVIDING APPLIANCES

It is well known that, in addition to its function as a metal-turning machine, the lathe can be applied to many other purposes. Although in a modern well-equipped machine shop it is usually found most efficient to confine lathes to their legitimate purpose, occasions do arise when time can be saved, or accuracy improved, by fitting a lathe for dealing with certain simple extraneous operations. This applies to the use of a lathe as a dividing machine, which enables work to be marked out and incised (or even more elaborate operations carried out) while it is set up for turning, and thus save time which would be required for setting up again for a second operation, besides avoiding the risk that it may not be perfectly true and concentric, which is always present when re-setting.

The term " dividing " refers to any method whereby a series of definite linear or circumferential measurements may be carried out, and thus applies equally to the marking out of a scale rule, or a protractor reading in degrees, the teeth of a gear wheel, or a number of bolting holes in a round flange. Circumferential dividing, however, which is the more common in lathe work, is generally defined by the specific term " indexing."

Linear dividing in the lathe is usually carried out by using the lead screws of the various slides as micrometers, and provided the latter are not badly worn, it can generally be

Fig. 42.—Micrometer index on screwcutting lathe—

carried out with fair accuracy, even on lathes that have no special claim to be considered as " precision " machine tools, so long as care is taken to eliminate backlash by taking all readings in one direction. Scales can be marked on cylindrical work mounted in the lathe, by using a point tool, such as a vee-thread screwcutting tool, to incise the surface over a part or the whole of a revolution, as required. If the slide screws are equipped with micrometer sleeves it is a very simple matter to feed them the required distance between divisions by direct

Fig. 43.—and scale incised by it on tailstock of lathe itself

measurement. Even when this facility is not provided, it is not difficult to fit a temporary or permanent indexing protractor to the lead screw operating handle.

For instance, a lead screw having 8 threads per inch may be graduated to read thousandths of an inch by fitting it with an index divided in 1/125th parts of a circle; a 10-thread lead screw requires a 1/100 scale, and so on. The wheel or disc on which the scale is marked should be as large in diameter as possible to produce an " open " scale reading.

Fig. 42 shows an example of a micrometer index fitted to a 3 in. screwcutting lathe of an inexpensive type. It was marked off with the aid of the indexing fixture shown in Fig. 46, and has proved extremely valuable in ordinary lathe operations, besides its special application to linear dividing. It has been used to incise a graduated scale on the tailstock barrel of the lathe itself, as shown in Fig. 43, and this item deserves inclusion in the list of useful lathe accessories dealt with in this book.

When marking off a scale, the increments of measurement should be resolved to the nearest thousandth of an inch, but in some cases it may be found more convenient to make up a special scale for the lead screw, indexed in a number of divisions to suit the scale to be marked, or to use the lathe change wheels as division plates. The problems involved are matters of simple arithmetic and need no detailed explanation here.

Should it be desired to mark off a flat scale, which cannot be incised by rotating it in the lathe, it may be attached to the saddle, and the point tool fitted in a rotating cutter bar and used in the manner of a fly-cutter. In many cases, however, it will be found unnecessary to rotate the bar, as the required depth of incision can be cut with a stationary tool, the lathe mandrel or the bar itself being in this case locked against rotation.

Methods similar to the above may be applied when it is necessary to drill a row of holes at exactly equal intervals along a piece of work, or to cut a number of equal-spaced notches or grooves, such as in rack cutting. It may, however, be found necessary to use some special milling or drilling fixture in the lathe when carrying out such work, and simple devices of this nature will be described in the next chapter.

Indexing methods

The value of some means of dividing the circumference of work has long been recognised by makers of light instrument and horological lathes, which are very often fitted with what is described as a " divided headstock," in which the large step of the driving pulley is drilled on the side or rim with one or more concentric circles of equally spaced holes, and a locking pin or detent provided on the fixed part of the headstock. In most cases the number of holes in the circles is designed to furnish multiples of the most commonly used divisions. Thus, a circle of 60 holes will provide multiples of 2, 3, 4, 6, 10, 12, 15, 20 and 30 divisions. This covers the majority of requirements in general practice, and when an occasion arises for an unusual number of divisions, the problem can generally be solved by fitting a special division plate on the tail end of the mandrel.

Engineers' lathes are not usually fitted with dividing gear by the makers, but it is generally easy to fit them with some simple arrangements for effecting the same purpose. In the case of screwcutting lathes the set of change wheels may be used very effectively as division plates, and are sufficiently accurate for most work likely to be undertaken—far more so than the most skilful use of dividers applied to the work, at any rate. Some kind of detent is necessary to engage the teeth of the wheel, which is, of course, keyed to the mandrel as it would be for setting up a screwcutting train.

A very simple method of effecting engagement with the change wheel teeth, which is applicable to most small screw-cutting lathes, is shown in Fig. 44. It comprises an eccentric disc, the edge of which is turned to fit tightly between the teeth of the wheel and to approximate tooth form, and has an eccentric hole for a stud by means of which it is attached to the side of a square bar. The latter is adapted to fit in the change-wheel quadrant or the reversing-stud slot of the headstock. It is adjusted so that the centre line of the disc falls in line with the radial centre line through the change wheel, and is engaged by turning round on its stud, the flynut on the latter enabling it to be locked in engagement.

Another indexing device for use in connection with change wheels (or with any accurately-cut gear wheels that can be adapted to fit the lathe mandrel) consists of a spring plunger with the end shaped to fit between the teeth of the wheel and carried in a bracket, which can be clamped to the change-wheel quadrant, or any other convenient part of the lathe headstock. The plunger must be a close fit in its guide so that there is no perceptible backlash when it is engaged

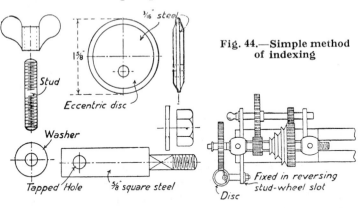

Fig. 44.—Simple method of indexing

with the teeth of the wheel. A device of this nature is shown in Fig. 45, and another, of essentially similar design, is seen in use in the photograph on the cover of this book.

The range of divisions obtainable from an indexing device may be enormously extended by worm-gearing it to the mandrel ; the increase, in fact, being equal to the ratio of worm reduction used. It is quite practicable to use a straight cut spur gear wheel (such as a change wheel) as a dividing worm wheel, by cutting a worm of a suitable pitch to engage with it, and mounting it on the change-wheel quadrant. A division plate and index pin are provided on the worm spindle, and the whole constitutes a device practically equal in utility to the universal dividing head used in milling practice. One very important advantage of a worm gear for

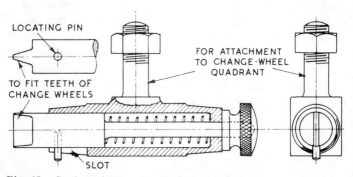

Fig. 45.—Spring plunger for direct indexing with change wheels

this purpose is that it is self-locking, so that the headstock spindle cannot move after being set for indexing, and no strain is placed on the indexing pin or division plate. If the worm is made so that its meshing depth with the wheel can be adjusted, all backlash between it and the wheel may be completely eliminated.

The worm geared dividing attachment shown in Fig. 46 is applicable to most small lathes. It employs a 60-toothed worm gear, mounted on the lathe mandrel, in conjunction with a single-start worm, the shaft of which is carried in a bracket mounted on the change wheel quadrant. (Worm gearing of guaranteed accuracy is obtainable commercially at reasonable cost, as it is extensively used in various kinds of transmission machinery.) One or more division plates, for concentric mounting on the outer boss of the wormshaft bracket, are provided, each having a number of circles,

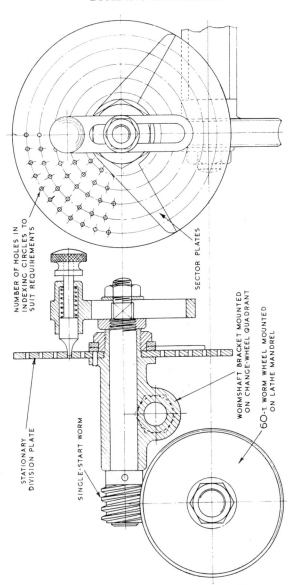

NUMBER OF HOLES IN
INDEXING CIRCLES TO
SUIT REQUIREMENTS

SECTOR PLATES

STATIONARY
DIVISION PLATE

SINGLE-START WORM

WORMSHAFT BRACKET MOUNTED
ON CHANGE-WHEEL QUADRANT

60-T. WORM WHEEL MOUNTED
ON LATHE MANDREL

Fig. 46.—A simple worm-geared indexing attachment for the lathe or milling machine

drilled with numbers of holes to suit the range of divisions likely to be required. A convenient selection for general work would be 100, 96, 84, 72 and 60 holes, but in horology or instrument work, it may be necessary to provide for more complicated dividing operations. For instance, clocks with monthly calendar movements may call for a wheel having a multiple of 31 teeth; this is a prime number which cannot be factorised. A year calendar, which requires a wheel having a multiple of 365, can be dealt with by a plate having 73 holes.

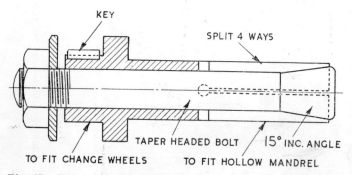

Fig. 47.—Extension mandrel for mounting change wheels when used for indexing

Methods of producing division plates, including those involving prime numbers, are fully described in the M.A.P. handbook *Milling in the Lathe*. Although the plates should obviously be drilled as accurately as possible, small errors can be tolerated, as they are reduced in proportion to the ratio of worm reduction. To simplify the counting of holes, a pair of sector plates, capable of being locked together, while freely rotatable on the boss of the bracket, are provided. They are set to span the number of holes required, and serve as a caliper or gauge to indicate the range of indexing pin movement at each shift.

The spring-loaded indexing pin, which is mounted on a radial arm capable of adjustment to suit the various rows of holes, must be retractable far enough to allow the pin to clear the sector plates when more than one complete revolution of the arm (i.e., more than 1/60 of one rotation of the worm wheel) is required. It may with advantage be provided with a bayonet catch or other device to hold it out of engagement while rotating the arm.

In many modern lathes, direct mounting of change wheels or worm gears on the lathe mandrel is precluded by the presence of the cluster or tumbler gearing for reversing the screwcutting gear train. As it is most important that the gears, when used for indexing, should be completely immune from lost motion or backlash, they can best be mounted on an extension adaptor fitted to the hollow mandrel of the lathe. As seen in Fig. 47, this consists of an expanding plug, split 3 or 4 ways for about half its length, and provided with a tapered bolt which locks it firmly in position and also clamps the change wheel in position. A key or dowel pin, as employed in the normal fitting of the wheels, may be used to prevent them positively from turning on the extension seating, but is not necessary if they are properly clamped by the nut and washer.

When it is not possible to obtain an orthodox worm gear for dividing, any accurate spur gears can be adapted to serve as worm gears. The worm should be made to correspond as closely as possible in pitch with the circumferential pitch of the change wheels, but small errors in this respect do not affect accuracy of indexing, so long as reasonably good meshing is ensured. It is advisable to set the worm shaft at such an angle relative to the plane of the wheel that the engaging worm teeth lie in line with the spur wheel teeth, but this is not absolutely necessary. The depth of mesh of the worm with the wheel is adjusted by swinging the change wheel quadrant.

CHAPTER V

SIMPLE MILLING ATTACHMENTS

When carrying out any kind of milling operation in the lathe, it is most important that the work should be held quite rigidly in an appropriate position to be operated on by the cutter. Most of the troubles and difficulties encountered in work of this nature are due to deficiencies in either or both respects. Any form of milling appliance which achieves facility of adjustment at the expense of rigidity, or vice versa, is open to serious objections from the practical point of view. It follows, therefore, that the simplest method of holding the work which gives the desired result is often the best.

It may be possible to clamp the work directly on the cross slide of the lathe by bolts and straps or clamping bars, and this method can be most highly recommended for rigidity, but some trouble may be experienced in adjusting the work exactly to the right height for operations that are critical in this respect. The usual and most obvious method is by means of packing slips, but in some cases, especially when no true reference face exists on which the work can be bedded down, this method may be insecure or otherwise unsuitable. In such cases, it is sometimes possible to clamp the work sideways to an angle plate mounted on the cross slide, and Fig. 49 shows how this method can be applied to the common operation of cutting an open keyway in a small machine spindle.

It is often necessary, however, to adjust or traverse the work vertically after mounting it up for milling, and for this purpose the use of a vertical slide mounted on the cross slide is the handiest method. Excellent vertical slides to fit lathes of all sizes are obtainable ready-made at quite moderate cost, and will be found a useful asset in any amateur or professional workshop. Their usefulness is sometimes greatly reduced by inadequate security in attaching them to the cross slide, which may totally defeat the efforts of the makers to produce a really rigid slide.

Where no specially made vertical slide is available, it is

sometimes possible to improvise one for light work by mounting the top slide of the lathe on an angle plate, with its traversing axis disposed vertically.

Light milling jobs on small work can often be accomplished by clamping it in the lathe tool post. This method is applic-

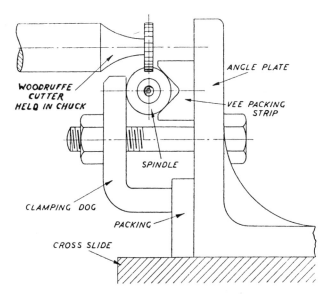

WOODRUFFE CUTTER HELD IN CHUCK

ANGLE PLATE

VEE PACKING STRIP

SPINDLE

CLAMPING DOG

PACKING

CROSS SLIDE

Fig. 49.—Work mounted on cross-slide for cutting keyway

able to facing the sides of square or polygonal bars, bolt heads, and so on, but the task of holding the work securely, and adjusting it to the correct angle, may be somewhat finicky. Closed keyways in small shafts may be cut by holding the work in this way, and the use of a vee packing strip under the work will be found helpful to hold the shaft securely and prevent it from rolling. The most difficult part of the operation in this case consists of packing the work up exactly to centre height to ensure that the keyway enters it squarely.

A simple device which ensures that round or polygonal
stock of any size is presented at the correct height is shown
in Fig. 50. It consists of a form of vee block, mounted on
its side, and provided with means of clamping the work in
it. In the example shown, the fitting is provided with a
slotted lug which is held down by the tool post bolt in the
place normally occupied by the pressure plate, but this
refinement can be omitted at the expense of some rigidity.
It is essential that the centre of the vee should coincide in
height with the lathe centres.

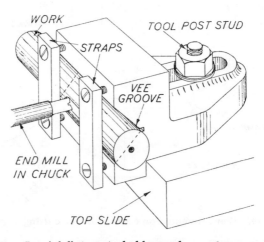

Fig. 50.—Special fixture to hold round or polygonal stock
for end milling

An extremely useful device for many kinds of milling
operations in the lathe is a small headstock which can be
mounted on the cross slide, with its spindle axis exactly
level with the lathe centres. The utility of this device is
still further enhanced if the spindle fitted to it is a replica
of the lathe mandrel in essential respects, particularly that
of the screwed nose. In this way, the lathe chucks can be
transferred to the spindle—with the work already set up in

them if necessary—for carrying out operations such as milling squares and hexagons, cross slotting and drilling, etc. The spindle is, of course, made rotatable, and may be fitted with a pulley so that it can be driven from overhead gear if occasion requires, but in any case it should be provided with some means of locking it securely. Any form of dividing

Fig. 51.—Small headstock mounted on cross-slide

gear that is applicable to the lathe mandrel may also be arranged to fit the auxiliary spindle.

A device of this nature, power-driven from overhead gear, and fitted with a fly cutter (which is practically a miniature version of that illustrated in Fig. 60, except that it is fitted to the taper socket of the spindle) is shown in Fig. 51, applied to generating a cam in the lathe. In this case the headstock was made from a scrap bearing bracket casting, and as its height did not conform with that of the lathe centres, it was adjusted by slips of packing under the foot.

A headstock of this type, mounted on the face of a standard type of angle plate or vertical slide, forms a simple but very practical gear-cutting attachment.

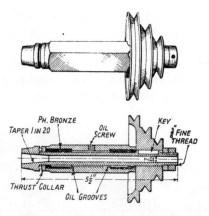

Fig. 52.—Simple drilling spindle

Milling and drilling spindles

Although, in a general way, the use of attachments requiring a power drive is outside the scope of this book, an exception may be made in respect of simple milling and drilling spindles, which are so useful as to deserve a place in the equipment of every general-purpose lathe. The appliance shown in Fig. 52 is quite simple to make, and incorporates many desirable features, including a ball thrust race and provision for adequate lubrication to cope with the requirements of high-speed running. A piece of square mild

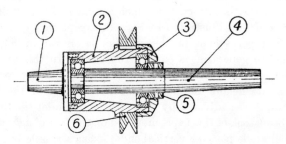

Fig. 53.—High-speed spindle for concentric drilling

steel is used for the body, and is bored right through and fitted with bronze bushes at each end. Oil channels should be cut in the bushes on the low-pressure side (i.e. opposite the direction towards which the spindle is pulled by the side thrust of the belt drive) and a central annular space is left to form an oil reservoir, which can be replenished through a screw hole in the body.

The spindle is made from tool steel, accurately turned and bored, with a socket to fit No. 1 Morse taper. If it is

Fig. 54.—Application of device shown in Fig. 53

impracticable to harden and grind the spindle, it should be carefully lapped to fit the bushes very closely, and the thrust race should in this case incorporate two separate washers instead of one of its elements being formed in the shoulder of the spindle nose, as shown in the drawing. It may be remarked that the parallel bearings shown, though slightly inferior to properly fitted double-cone bearings, are very much easier to make and fit, and will be found quite satisfactory for most purposes. The taper socket of the spindle may be fitted with an adaptor to take split collet chucks, which will greatly extend the utility of the device. It is most important that the square body should be made of sufficiently heavy section material to avoid being distorted when it is clamped in the tool post.

The spindle may be driven by means of the usual overhead pulley, or from a small independent motor mounted at the back of the lathe. Its scope of usefulness includes milling and precision-drilling of work mounted in the lathe, drilling of division plates with the aid of indexing gear fitted to the lathe mandrel, and also internal and external cylindrical grinding. The latter operations, however, require an exceptionally high spindle speed, which is extremely difficult to obtain by belt drive, and it is a moot point whether it is really desirable to use the lathe for such purposes.

The device shown in Figs. 53 and 54 is not a milling appliance in the strict sense of the term ; it is intended only for concentric drilling, and is applied to the tailstock socket ; the drive is again taken from overhead gear or any other conveniently placed source of power. It will be seen from Fig. 54 that the stub 7, which carries the drill chuck, is attached to an internally bored housing 2 fitted with two ball races. A ring nut 3, screwed on the rear end of the housing serves the triple purpose of retaining the driving pulley 6, locating the rear ball race and protecting the latter from the ingress of foreign matter. The shank 4 is tapered to fit in the tailstock socket and extended to form a stationary mounting for the ball races. End thrust is taken, through the rear race, against the thrust collar 5.

A drilling spindle of this type is extremely useful for deep drilling in the lathe, particularly when very small diameter drills have to be used, as it enables them to be run at much higher speed than is usually possible, not only expediting the operation and assisting in clearing the swarf, but also tending to keep the hole perfectly true. It can be applied to best advantage in a tailstock fitted with sensitive lever feed.

Vertical milling attachment

Fig. 55 shows how a small drilling machine may be adapted

for use as a vertical milling attachment in the lathe, using the lathe mandrel as a source of power. The drilling machine must have good quality bearings, and also some means of locking the vertical feed when it has been adjusted to suit

Fig. 55.—Small drilling machine used as milling attachment

the cut. The rig shown in the photo was set up in order to carry out a rather elaborate profile milling job, using a master template or stencil to guide the cutter ; and it performed the operation satisfactorily and efficiently.

CHAPTER VI

STEADYING APPLIANCES

MANY operations are encountered in lathe practice where it becomes necessary to compensate for an inherent lack of rigidity in the work, by the use of some form of " steady rest." The most common example occurs when long slender shafts are turned between centres, or overhanging a long way from the chuck. Many lathes are provided with steadies as part of their standard or supplementary equipment, the usual forms being the fixed or " three-point " steady, and the travelling or " two-point " steady. The former is clamped to the bed of the lathe, and embodies three equally spaced pads, capable of radial adjustment to suit the diameter of the work ; the latter is attached to the saddle or carriage of the lathe, so that it moves with it, maintaining a constant position relative to the tool, and carries two steady pads or rollers, which can be adjusted to bear on the top and back of the work respectively. In some cases, the two separate pads are replaced by a single vee steady pad, which is adjustable diagonally, so that both jaws make contact with the work.

The three-point steady is extremely useful for such purposes as steadying the end of a long bar or tube, held at the other extremity in the chuck, for centring, boring, etc., or for supporting the centre of a long, thin shaft mounted between centres. It is necessary to adjust the pads of the steady so that they make contact with the work with even pressure, and do not force it away from its normal concentric running axis. Any form of steady requires a true and smooth surface on the portion of the work where it is applied, and the pads must be kept copiously lubricated to avoid seizure. The travelling steady may be set so as to traverse the work ahead of the cutting tool, or to follow behind it, according to which is the more convenient for the nature of the work or operation. In most cases, it is found that the latter position is preferable, especially when taking the first cut on previously unmachined stock, as any roughness or inaccuracy of the latter would affect the truth of the cut if the steady preceded the tool. The steady pads must be adjusted to the work for each new cut, as the diameter of the work is reduced.

A form of steady for round bars, which is not very common in engineering practice at the present day, but has always been popular for horological work, consists of a steel disc having a circle of tapered holes of various stock sizes around its edge. This disc is clamped, by a centre pivot bolt, to a standard which can be mounted on the lathe bed, so that either of the tapered holes can be brought in line with the concentric axis of the work. The most useful function of this device, in the lathes with which we are mainly concerned, is to steady bars for centring, but it should be noted that it can only be relied upon to hold them dead truly when their ends are square with the axis and free from burrs.

In cases where no suitable form of steady is provided in the equipment of the lathe, it is nearly always possible to improvise a fairly effective substitute. For instance, if it is required to steady a piece of steel bar, a hole of the appropriate size may be drilled and reamered in an odd piece of flat bar or plate, and the latter clamped to the lathe bed by any convenient means, so that the hole is concentric with the lathe axis. If the work is to be centred or axially drilled from the tailstock, the steady bar may be held in the tool post, and it is convenient to hold it thus for drilling also, thereby ensuring that the hole is concentrically true. This method obviously cannot be applied when the work must be supported by the steady for outside turning ; in this case, the steady bar or plate may be clamped to the vertical face of an angle plate mounted either on the lathe bed or the saddle.

Steadying devices are often applied from the tool post of the lathe for the purpose of correcting rough or inaccurate centres in shafts, or preventing the tip of a drill from wandering when entering the work. The steady in this case is usually nothing more than a piece of steel bar—often one of the lathe tools, turned end for end, is used (Figs. 56 and 57). It is, however, most important that the end face of the bar should be quite smooth and true, so as to bear evenly on the work, or the lips of the drill. When correcting centres, a square centre, with keen cutting edges, should be used in the tailstock, and no attempt should be made to force the pace. Both the steady and the square centre should be well lubricated, the former with machine oil and the latter with an approved cutting compound.

The simple bar steady may be improved by making a vee-notch in the end, so that it bears on the work at two points 90 degrees apart, or by equipping it with either one or two rollers. In either case, the contact surfaces should be dead smooth, and hardened. A roller steady is an

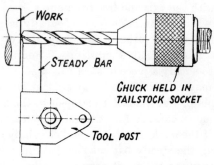

Fig. 56

extremely useful tool for truing up flat discs held in the lathe
chuck.   In this case it is presented square with the surface
of the work, near its outer edge, as shown in Fig. 58, and the

Fig.   57. — Lathe
tool, turned end
for end, used as
steady

chuck is only partially tightened.   By feeding the roller
up against the work, any wobble that may be present will
be corrected in the course of a few revolutions of the lathe
mandrel ; the steady may then be removed, and the chuck
fully tightened, before proceeding with machining the disc.

The necessity for using a drill supported on the back centre
for drilling in the lathe, does not often arise in modern practice, as most lathes are equipped with tailstock drill chucks,

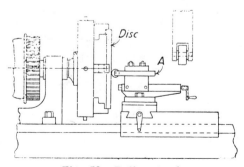

Fig. 58.—Roller steady

but sometimes a drill of a size outside the capacity of the chuck must be used, and then the only course is to revert to this method. Some difficulty may, however, be experienced through the tendency of the drill to wander from the centre when starting, even when all precautions are taken to keep it central. In some cases, it is found that a steady presented vertically to support the tip of the drill is the most practical remedy, and Fig. 59 shows a steady of this type that can be fitted to the socket of the hand rest, or any other convenient socket that can be mounted on the lathe cross slide. The device consists of a short bar with a vee notch in the end, screwed throughout most of its length with a fine thread, and fitted with a large diameter knurled or serrated nut, by means of which it can be adjusted up or down to suit the diameter in the drill. In addition to its use as a steady, this device also forms a very useful bottlejack, to adjust the elevation of work for marking out or machining.

Other forms of steadies

In addition to the devices described above, there are many other types of steadies applicable to various kinds of lathe work. Production lathes are often fitted with tool holders incorporating special steadying devices. These are most common in capstan tools, but also are applied to tools used in the slide rest. An example of a tool incorporating

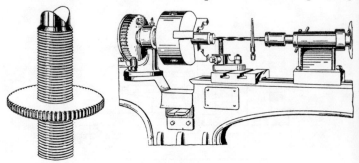

Fig. 59.

its own steady is seen in the parting tool described in Fig. 28 (Chapter III). The use of a bush steady, which fits over an already machined projecting end of chucked work, and is held by the tailstock, may assist in solving difficult problems in machining ; or it may be found convenient to apply a pilot or " plug " steady inside a bored hole in the work, and similarly mounted in the tailstock socket. When finishing bores by means of a sizing cutter in the tailstock, a pilot steady on the end of the bar, fitting the partly machined bore, may improve accuracy and finish, or in some cases it may be better to extend the pilot to fit inside the bore of the hollow mandrel of the lathe.

The many ingenious steadying devices employed in capstan lathe practice are well worth studying, as they may often be applied to the solution of very difficult problems in the operation of other types of lathes. It should be remembered that the proper use of steadies will not only enable heavy cuts to be taken on light work, and thereby enable work to be speeded up, but also enable accuracy to be improved, and risk of accidents to the work or the tools to be reduced to the minimum.

CHAPTER VII

VARIOUS FORMS OF CUTTERS

GENERALLY speaking, the use of any standard form of milling cutter, as supplied for use on ordinary milling machines, is equally applicable to milling in the lathe, and the arrangements for mounting and driving the cutters are identical. End and face mills must of necessity be attached to the mandrel, either by chucking or by a taper shank fitting the centre socket. In the former case, a split collet chuck is to be preferred, as it generally enables the shank of the cutter to be held more truly than other types of chucks, and often more firmly ; the overhang of the cutter beyond the mandrel bearings is also reduced, and the minimum interference with accessibility and visibility ensured. Taper-fitted cutters may sometimes be unsatisfactory through working loose under the effect of heavy cuts or vibration, and it may be advisable to drill and tap the end of the shank to take a drawbolt, which passes through the hollow mandrel of the lathe and can be pulled up tightly with a nut at the tail end.

Other types of cutters, which cut only or mainly on the periphery, may be mounted on arbors and held in the same way, but it is generally advantageous to support the outer end of the arbor with the tailstock centre, and in many cases they need not be chucked at all, but may be run between the lathe centres. This applies in particular to the use of circular saws, which are extensively applied in the lathe for various purposes, such as slotting screw-heads, splitting clamping lugs or bearings, and even in some cases for the accurate parting off of short lengths of stock.

In many cases where it is desired to carry out milling operations in the lathe, difficulty may be experienced in obtaining a suitable cutter for the required purpose. Quite efficient cutters for occasional jobs may, however, be made up at short notice, and with very little trouble. Several types of such cutters are described in the handbook *Milling in the Lathe,* and it is not considered necessary to go deeply into the subject here, but one or two simple and very useful forms of cutters may be considered of general interest.

One of these is a modified form of single-toothed or " fly "

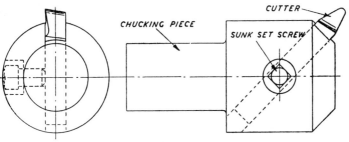

Fig. 60.—Modified '' fly '' cutter

cutter that will be found extremely useful for facing the sides of castings which for any reason cannot readily be dealt with by the usual method of mounting on the angle plate or faceplate. It consists, as shown in Fig. 60, of a special form of holder, in which a short lathe tool may be mounted so as to be capable of serving as a side and face milling cutter. The holder is of robust proportions so as to hold the tool quite rigidly, and may be held in the three-jaw chuck, or, better still, internally screwed so as to screw directly on the mandrel nose. By diagonally mounting it in this way, the cutter is capable not only of cutting both on the face and the periphery, but is also adjustable in respect of its radial

sweep, so that it will deal with material of various face
widths, and in some cases avoids the necessity of adjusting
the elevation of the work.   The most suitable form of cutter
for most jobs is one having a fairly narrow rounded nose, as
shown, but other shapes may be used to suit the work in
hand ; rake and clearance angles are the same as used in
ordinary lathe tools, according to the material being
machined.

Simple reamers and cutters

Although not classified exclusively as lathe accessories,
several kinds of reamers and cutters are often required in
lathe work, and though most of them can be obtained
ready-made, they are relatively expensive, and hardly
justified for occasional use. Simple home-made tools, which
can be produced in a few minutes, are capable of quite useful
work and are not limited to standard shapes and sizes.
They can be made from silver steel rod, which is obtainable
from tool dealers, and are hard and durable enough for
most of their duties, even at high speed, if properly heat
treated.   Full details of this treatment are given in the
M.A.P. handbook *Hardening and Tempering Engineers' Tools*.
Still better results can be obtained by using high-speed
steel bar, but this is difficult to anneal to a machinable state,
and is generally shaped by grinding only.

The term " broach," in modern engineering practice, is
usually applied to a tool which is pulled through the bore
of a wheel or collar to produce keyways or splines, or to the
outside of work in a similiar axial order of movement.   But
originally it was used to define a primitive kind of reamer,
sometimes produced by grinding facets on a round bar to
form obtuse-angled cutting edges.   Clockmakers still use
this tool in an improved form, as shown in Fig. 61, to open
out pivot holes in clock plates for fitting bushes or *bouchons*
to compensate for wear.   The broaches usually have five
cutting edges, and are tapered up to one or two degrees,

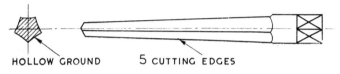

HOLLOW GROUND 5 CUTTING EDGES

CLOCKMAKER'S BROACH

Fig. 61.

though they could be made parallel, with a slightly tapered
lead at the end, if required. Hollow grinding of the facets,
as shown, not only increases the cutting efficiency, but also
enables the edges to be honed to restore the keen edge
when worn. The grinding operation can be carried out in
the lathe, using a small diameter wheel in a grinding spindle
or flexible-shaft handpiece and indexing the tool blank. For
very small broaches, it may be necessary to use a wood or
fibre pad at the back to serve as a steady.

The tool known as a " toolmaker's broach," for finishing
small parallel holes, deserves to be better known than it is.
It consists simply of a tool steel rod turned or lapped to the
size required and ground off at an angle of about 10 degrees
to well below half its diameter at the extreme end, as shown
in Fig. 62. Sometimes the end is ground right to a point,

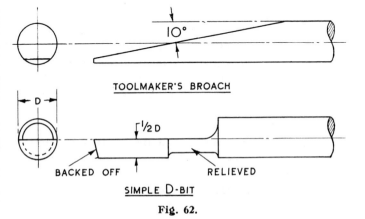

10°

TOOLMAKER'S BROACH

D

½ D

BACKED OFF RELIEVED

SIMPLE D-BIT

Fig. 62.

but this is no advantage. The tool is in fact a form of D-bit, with very limited cutting clearance, which diminishes progressively until it becomes merely a burnisher at the large end. It is generally made only in small sizes, up to about $\frac{3}{16}$ in. dia., and used only to take out 2 to 3 thousandths of an inch.

The orthodox form of D-bit, also shown in Fig. 62, is equally useful, though some engineers at the present day have not heard of it. Many versions of it have been made; it can be adapted to drilling holes from the solid, but is best suited to finishing holes drilled slightly undersize, and opened out to size at the mouth by boring or reaming. Its rigidity helps in producing truly straight holes, and having little or no cutting clearance, it does not tend to chatter or produce non-circular holes. The front edge is backed off both horizontally and vertically, so that it cuts on the front corner only, and any regrinding necessary should be done on this face. A slight radius on the nose helps to produce a good finish. Unlike standard reamers, which need to be tapered on the end, D-bits produce a parallel finish on blind bores.

As a cutting tool, the D-bit is relatively inefficient, and lacks chip clearance, but a relief behind the front of the cutaway portion as shown helps in this respect. Frequent backing-out is, however, always necessary to prevent clogging. The amount of cutaway is sometimes varied, and the side edges are sometimes relieved or backed off, but generally speaking, the best results are obtained by cutting the round bar away to exactly half its diameter as shown.

Countersinking tools

The chamfering of holes to fit the heads of countersunk screws is not necessarily a lathe operation, though similar operations often occur in lathe work. Twist drills are often used for countersinking, but are not well suited to this purpose; the normal cutting angle of a drill is much too

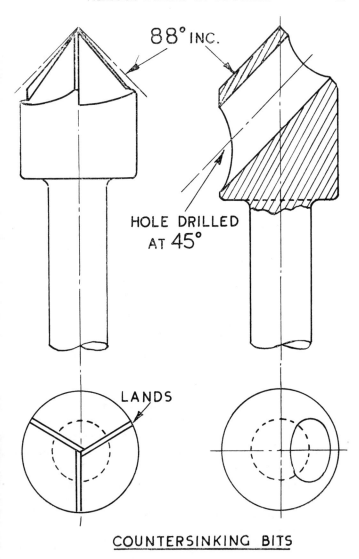

88° INC.

HOLE DRILLED
AT 45°

LANDS

COUNTERSINKING BITS

Fig. 63.—Two forms of countersinking bits for use in the lathe
or drilling machine

obtuse for fitting screws properly, but even if this is corrected, the rake is too fierce, and tends to make the drill snatch, chatter or cut out of round. Nearly all two-bladed counter-sinking tools have this tendency to some extent, but a broken centre-drill, ground to approximately 90 degrees at the point, works better by reason of its rigidity.

The cheap countersinking tools obtainable commercially are generally of the " rose-bit " type, which rarely produce a really clean cut, due to the incorrect cutting angles of their individual edges. Chattering is a very prevalent fault in all countersinking operations, especially when the work or the tool is run at high speed, and it is often recommended that speed should be reduced to below 100 r.p.m. for this work. But the trouble can be avoided by eliminating all front rake on the cutting edges of the tool, and reducing cutting clearance to the minimum.

D-bits, formed to the correct angle, make fairly good countersinks, especially if provided with pilots to fit the hole. In general, the fewer the cutting edges the better. The three-edged cutter shown in Fig. 63 has been found to work very cleanly and efficiently, and the same drawing shows a rather unusual type in which a single cutting edge is formed by drilling a hole through the blank, perpendicular to the bevel angle. It works with practically zero clearance, so that it is free from chatter, and may be run in either direction. Though the angle of standard countersunk screws is 90 degrees, it is best to make the countersink slightly more acute, to ensure that the screw head fits closely at the top face.

The type of cutter generally known as a " pin drill," is not truly classifiable as a milling cutter, as it is intended to cut only on the end face, and is usually provided with a pilot or guide pin to work in a previously drilled hole. In its common form, it is made as shown in Fig. 64, with the pilot machined integral with the actual cutter, which is milled or filed flat, and backed off to provide cutting edges.

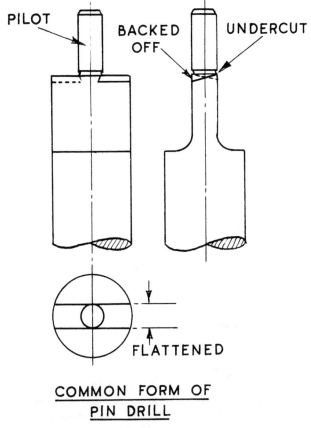

COMMON FORM OF
PIN DRILL

Fig. 64.

It is usual to undercut the root of the pilot slightly so that
the edges can be carried as close to the centre as possible
and avoid leaving a burr or ridge around the hole to be
faced. Such cutters work quite well, but the pilot is liable
to be brittle, as it cannot easily be selectively tempered,
and may break off in the hole. Cutters with inserted pilots
of soft steel are generally more durable.

Two examples of such cutters, which can easily be made from round tool steel bar, are shown in Fig. 65, which also illustrates how they are made. After facing the end of the bar, and drilling the hole for the pilot, saw cuts are made across the end face to a depth equal to about one quarter the diameter. This is easier in the first example, as the cuts can run straight across; in the second case, they must be made at an angle. But it is generally found that cutters

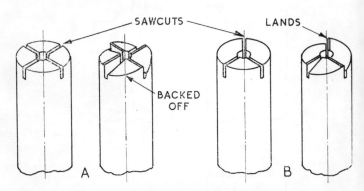

Fig. 65.—Four-toothed and three-toothed facing cutters for use with inserted pilots

with an odd number of teeth produce the cleanest and most accurate results. It is not necessary to space the cutting edges accurately, as uneven spacing has often proved an advantage in reducing the tendency to chatter; but they must be at uniform level.

The cutting edges are filed as shown at an angle of about 20 to 30 degrees to the face, leaving a slight " land " at the extreme tip which can be honed with an oilstone slip, after hardening and tempering the cutter. No details of the pilot pins are shown in the drawing, but they are made a tight push fit in the centre holes of the cutters, and their outer ends may be of any size to suit the holes which have to be faced.

Small facing cutters may be made from stock tool steel bar of appropriate size, provided that this can be held in the size of chuck used, but for larger cutters it may be necessary to turn down the shank, or to economise tool steel by making the cutter itself short, and drilling and tapping it to screw on to a small mild steel shank. Cutters below $\frac{1}{4}$ in. dia. should be turned down on the cutting end from $\frac{1}{4}$ in. material for a short distance only, to maintain maximum rigidity and enable them to be held securely in standard chucks.

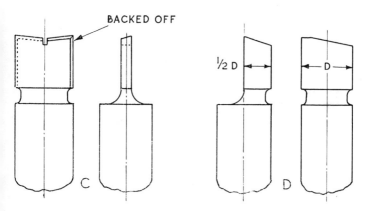

Fig. 66.—Two-bladed and single bladed end mills

The form of cutter shown can be made to work as an end mill by backing off the sides of the cutting edges and omitting the pilot hole, but they are not so easy to adapt in this way as flat two-edged cutters. End mills differ from facing cutters in being capable of working with traversing movement, and side teeth are therefore essential. The simple flat cutter shown in Fig. 66 will give excellent service in cutting keyways, grooves, flutes, or steam engine cylinder ports. In the small sizes, it must be run at very high speed to cut efficiently, and the highest speed normally provided on metal turning lathes is barely adequate for best performance. In rotary spindles which can be run at speeds of 3 or 4 thousand r.p.m., they work much better, and the single-point cutter—actually a form of D-bit—can also be used for end milling. The type of two-edged cutter known as a " slot drill," having the cutting edges so designed that it is capable of deep feeding, or even drilling from solid, is not easy to make in the home workshops, but its advantages apply mainly in industrial work where fast cutting is essential to efficient production.

Flat cutters or D-bits can easily be made with radiused or tapered cutting edges for channelling or fluting to special shapes, and they can be honed to keep them in keen condition more easily than multi-toothed cutters. When making any kind of cutter by milling or filing, sharp internal corners should be avoided wherever possible, and scores or file-marks removed, as these may form a focus for cracks during the hardening and tempering processes.

Multi-toothed cutters for side and face milling can be made by inserting a number of short tool bits in axial, radial or oblique holes drilled in a mild steel hub. There is rarely any advantage in using more than six bits, and they must be accurately set to extend to a uniform distance so that they share the work evenly. A good way to ensure this is to set them up and grind them in position in a cylindrical grinder, or a tool and cutter grinder if available. In the case of silver steel, they can be turned over the edges before hardening, and backed off by hand. It is necessary to clamp the bits securely, using Allen (high tensile socketed) grub-screws, bearing on flats or indentations in the shanks; other methods, such as serrated wedges, as used in some inserted-tooth cutters, are difficult to apply in the small workshop.

It is always a problem to keep any kinds of multi-tooth cutters really sharp unless the proper equipment for regrinding them is available. It is not beyond the means of the competent turner to adapt a small lathe or grinder for this purpose, but special grinding wheels are necessary, and they must be trued with a diamond tool. Except where the maximum rate of metal removal is essential, there are many advantages in using cutters with the minimum number of teeth, which can easily be honed or ground when necessary.

CHAPTER VIII

AIDS TO SCREWCUTTING

ONE of the most valuable properties of the engineer's lathe is its ability to generate threads of various pitches by the use of a lead screw or master screw, geared to rotate at a suitable ratio to the lathe mandrel. A description of the methods and technique of screwcutting is not within the scope of this book ; it is fully dealt with in *Practical Lessons in Metal Turning and Screwcutting* and also in the *M.E. Lathe Manual*. However, one or two simple devices which can be used to facilitate or simplify screw-cutting operations are well worthy of mention.

Many lathe operators—not always mere novices, either—find difficulty in ensuring that, after disengaging the lead screw at the end of a run, it can be re-engaged so that the relative location of the tool with the pitch of the thread is the same each time—in other words, " picking up the thread." This problem does not arise where the pitch of the thread cut is a multiple of the lead screw pitch, but can be troublesome in threads of odd pitches. It can be side-tracked by avoiding disengagement of the lead screw, and running the lathe backwards to return the tool to its starting point, which is easy enough for short threads, especially with treadle lathes, or power lathes with reversing gear. It may, however, be slow and tedious for long threads, and it may also entail some risk of unscrewing the chuck or driver plate ; for this reason, the practice is not generally favoured by experienced turners, and is often considered ethically wrong.

The best-known and most practical device for ensuring proper re-engagement of screwcutting gear is the mechanical indicator, which is incorporated in the standard design of many lathes, and obtainable as an extra attachment in others. As it is a relatively inexpensive device, it is hardly worth while to construct it, unless for any reason, such as uncommon pitch of lead screw, or unsuitable design of lathe saddle, the available fittings cannot be used.

Many lathe users, however, have made and fitted these indicators, so a brief description of their construction is not out of place. In all cases, they embody a worm-geared spindle arranged vertically or near-vertically, often with means of disengagement from the lead screw when not in use, and fixed laterally in relation to the lathe saddle. The worm gear must have a number of teeth which is a multiple of the threads per inch of the lead screw. The top end of the spindle carries a dial marked with divisions corresponding with the number of teeth in the worm wheel, or alternatively, a pointer in conjunction with a similar number of index marks on a fixed surrounding disc. (Fig. 67.)

Assuming that the lead screw is of 8 t.p.i., and the worm wheel has 16 teeth, engagement of the lead screw may safely be effected at any point for threads of 8, 16, 24, 32 t.p.i. and so on for all multiples of 8. For 4, 12, 20 t.p.i. etc., the lead screw can be engaged at eight positions on the dial ; for 2, 6, 10, 14 t.p.i. etc., one mark in four gives correct meshing position. Any whole number of t.p.i. allows of meshing in two places, at opposite points on the dial, and for numbers involving halves, one position only is possible. The device could be made to cover quarters as well, by doubling the number of teeth in the worm wheel, but this is rarely necessary in ordinary engineering practice.

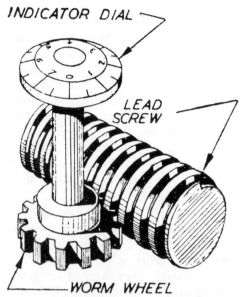

INDICATOR DIAL

LEAD SCREW

WORM WHEEL

Fig. 67. Mechanical screwcutting indicator

When fitting and using a device of this nature, it is most important to ensure that on the first engagement of the lead screw, one of the marks on the dial lines up *exactly* with the fixed index mark (or *vice versa*), otherwise errors in engagement are possible.   If the dial is fixed in relation to the worm wheel, this may entail the fitting of shims to the bearing bracket by which the device is attached to the saddle, in order to line up the marks correctly; but once adjusted in this respect, it should on no account be altered unless and until any alteration to the saddle or clasp unit makes this necessary.

This form of indicator is applicable to all lathes in which the saddle can be disengaged from the lead screw; but some of the simpler screwcutting lathes have the lead screw permanently engaged by means of a fixed nut, and a simple dog clutch is used to couple the lead screw to the train of gear wheels used for screwcutting. In such cases, the positions for engaging the clutch can only be indicated by some means of locating the relative positions of the lathe mandrel and the lead screw. The old method of doing so was by making chalk marks on the collar of the mandrel (or the gear wheel attached to it) and the driven member of the lead screw clutch, but this was crude and inexact, often leading to disastrous errors. A rather unusual, but thoroughly effective, method of ensuring correct juxtaposition of mandrel and lead screw is by fitting electric contacts to each member so that a lamp or bell circuit is closed when, and only when, both arrive simultaneously at the correct position for engagement (Fig. 68.)

In making or adapting tools for screwcutting, the most important consideration is to ensure that the flanks of the tool are ground to the correct angle, and highly finished, to ensure accuracy and smoothness of the threads produced. This of course applies only to vee, acme and other " formed "

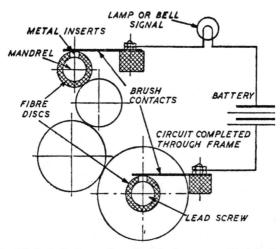

Fig. 68. Wiring diagram for electrical screwcutting indicator

threads ; square threads require similar attention to the front edge, but the sides may with advantage have both side and back clearance, except where the tool is narrower than the thread form, and used as a side cutting tool to finish the groove to correct width ; this is often desirable for coarse threads.

To ensure good finish of the thread form, there is much to be said for the use of disc forming tools, on the same principle as that shown in Fig. 31. The flanks can be turned to exactly the correct angle (55 deg. inclusive for all Whitworth form threads) and oilstoned to a high finish, after which the form is maintained throughout the life of the tool, as it needs grinding only on the top cutting face. It is practicable to make a set of disc tools to give exactly correct crest and root forms, but it is permissible, except in the case of very exacting work, such as gauge-making, to use one tool for cutting a fairly wide range of pitches, as the root radius is relatively unimportant, and the crest is best finished with a chaser or standard die nut. Machine chasers can also be made of disc form, by similar methods.

By mounting a disc tool in a holder or shank offset at half the included angle of the flank, as shown in Fig. 69, it is well adapted to the highly efficient method of feeding the tool in at the flank angle, thus relieving the load on the tool point and enabling top rake to be used to good effect.

When cutting threads of coarse pitch, it is important to ensure that proper side clearance is given on the tool, and obviously this should be related, not to the vertical face of the tool, but to the lead angle of the thread to be cut. (Note that this depends not on the actual pitch alone, but also on the diameter of the work.) A simple gauge which facilitates grinding and setting of the tool may be made quite easily from two small pieces of flat gauge plate, or old saw blade, and may be combined with a fixed angle gauge for testing the tool form and setting the tool point square with the work (Fig. 70). The angular graduations can be engraved,

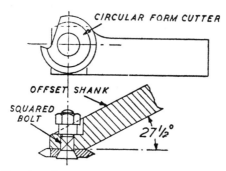

Fig. 69. Circular form screwcutting tool, with offset shank to suit Whitworth form threads

or etched with nitric acid, but even without these markings, a gauge of this type will be extremely useful for many purposes, and it can be set by reference to the angle of a sample thread, in most cases. Incidentally, the use of a circular shank, held in a split holder as used for boring bars, would enable the lead angle of a screwcutting tool to be adjusted after grinding.

Lathes which are not equipped for screw generating in the normal way have often been successfully adapted to producing threads by the addition of simple attachments. The most common, and probably the most satisfactory, of these is that which employs a rotating " hob " or master thread to traverse the cutting tool (either a single-point tool or a

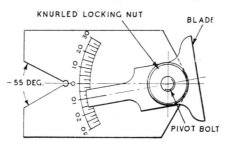

Fig. 70. Simple rake gauge

chaser) by the engagement of a suitable follower, such as a
segment of a nut. (Fig. 71.) There are many forms of the
" hob and drag " device, and it is still a standard fitting in
certain types of production lathes ; the usual arrangement
is to mount the hob at the outer end of the mandrel, and
fit a shaft parallel with the latter, having arms at its extremities to carry the follower and the cutting tool, so that
they can be swung into engagement simultaneously.   A
limit stop on the arm serves as a depthing or sizing adjustment, and it is also possible to arrange a quick-release or
run-out at the end of the thread.

This principle of operation has been adapted in a very
simple way by mounting a screwed bush or collar on the
shaft to be threaded (or otherwise co-axial with the work)
and using this as an extemporised hob ; the follower can
be a segment cut from a suitable nut, and attached to the
tool by a short, adjustable bar (Fig. 72). As the slide-rest
traverse cannot be used for this kind of operation, the feed
screw of the top slide may be removed to enable it to slide
freely; more often, however, the hand rest is used, and the
entire operation is controlled by hand.   While this may
appear to be a precarious sort of device to manipulate, calling
for a good deal of skill, it has been quite extensively used in

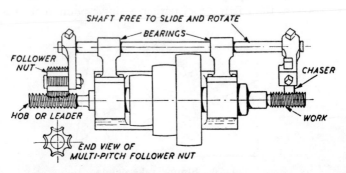

Fig. 71. Chasing attachment, using hob and follower

the past for the commercial production of cheap screwed
components such as gas fittings.

Many small parts are screwed or tapped in the lathe
by the use of taps and dies, and in order to obtain the best
possible accuracy with these, it is highly desirable to provide
means of ensuring positively the concentric and axial truth
of the threads. For holding taps, the tailstock chuck is
fairly satisfactory, and tailstock die holders for standard
sizes of circular dies are obtainable from manufacturers of
lathes and accessories.

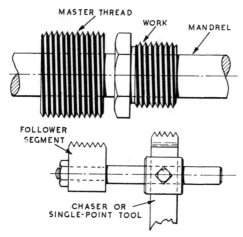

Fig. 72. Improvised chasing device

It is, however, possible to improve on these appliances
without making them necessarily complicated or elaborate.
One very desirable improvement would be a means of
limiting the torque which can be applied to the tool, to
avoid the risk of breakage if it becomes clogged or overloaded.
In industrial production, the use of overload clutches for
machine taps and dies is very common, but they have to be
separately adjusted for each size of tool, and as this can
only be done by trial, it is not practicable for one-off jobs.

A simpler method, which is generally satisfactory if used with discretion, is to make the actual tap or die holder independent of the tailstock fitting, and control the torque applied by hand. For small taps and dies, a " floating " holder knurled on the outside, and loose on or in the shank which is socketed in the tailstock, is satisfactory, but for larger sizes, a lever or tommy bar may have to be added. The latter, however, while providing sensitive control, lacks the ability to be quickly released if there is imminent danger of overload.

A form of holder which is much used on production lathes is that which provides for releasing the tap or die completely when a given depth of thread is released. The usual form of " slip " holder comprises a floating sleeve driven by pins or keys on the fixed shank, having a limited depth of engagement. The driving pins should not be rounded or bevelled at the end. Normally, these hold the sleeve against rotation, and so long as the shank is fed forward, constitute a positive drive ; but if the forward traverse of the shank is stopped, the sleeve continues to move forward as the thread is cut, and runs off the pins. When used on capstan or automatic lathes, the shank has a limited traverse, controlled by stops on the tool slide or other means, and this disengages the holder at a definite point, so that it can be set to produce exactly the length of thread required.

In small centre lathes, it is not usually practicable to fit limit stops on the tailstock feed, but the same principle of controlling the depth of thread can be applied in the holder illustrated in Fig. 73. This is done by fitting a limit stop inside the hollow shank, so that at a set depth, it makes contact with the end of the rod being screwed, and thereby arrests the travel, so that the loose sleeve runs out of engagement with the driving pins. Allowance for the length of the latter must be made when setting the stop, which is locked by a set screw in the shank. For very short threads, the end of the stop is reduced in size so that it can pass into the die.

This stop device is not applicable to a tap holder, but the same principle could be applied to limiting the depth of internal threads by fitting an adjustable stop rod to the fixed portion of the shank, with a fork to engage with the end face of the work at the appropriate point. (Fig. 74.)

Tap holders are usually required to hold various sizes of shanks, and to avoid the necessity for expensive and cumbersome chucks, the usual method is to make the body of the holder with a socket to take split bushes or collets, which can easily be made as required to take the size of tap in use. The grip can be applied by a side grub screw, or any other convenient manner ; a frictional grip which is capable of slipping in emergency is better than a positive drive, such as provided by an internal square or key.

Most tapping and threading operations call for much lower mandrel speeds than are used for ordinary turning, and in many cases the use of the back gear is desirable. Often, however, it is not prudent to use power drive at all, and

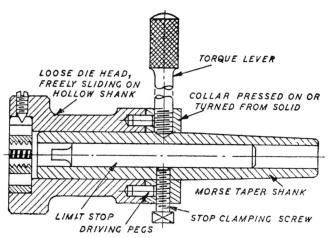

Fig. 73. Tailstock die holder

many light or delicate operations can be carried out safer, and even more expeditiously, by pulling the lathe chuck round by hand. Some users have made hand cranks which can be applied to the mandrel for this purpose, or alternatively, to the operation of tap or die holders at the tailstock end, the headstock meanwhile being locked against rotation in this case. The value of any such device will depend largely on the particular conditions of working, and where production time is an important factor, most operators find that anything which needs to be specially rigged is hardly worth while, unless it can be used for a run of repetition work.

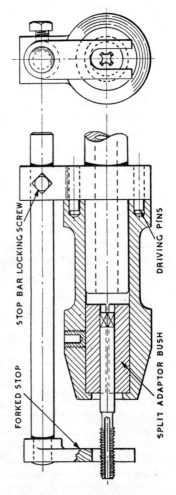

Fig. 74.   Slip tap holder

CHAPTER IX

MISCELLANEOUS ACCESSORIES

Combination turning tools

THE once familiar " tool pad," consisting of a hollow wooden
handle containing a set of " bits " intended to serve respectively as gimlet, bradawl, screwdriver, and so on, and adapted
to fit in a pin chuck at the end of the handle, has very much
declined in popularity nowadays, mainly because most of the
tools of this nature were so " cheap and nasty " as to be
of little use to a practical craftsman. But there is no denying
the soundness of the idea, where a number of small tools are
required to be kept handy for use in the minimum possible

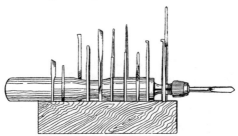

Fig. 75.—Set of small hand turning tools with pin chuck mounted
in wooden handle.

space, and it can be usefully adapted to a set of hand turning
tools for turning wood, ivory, or ornamental metal work.
This not only saves the space occupied by a full set of
normally handled tools, but also much of the expense or

trouble of making them, and economises in the use of tool steel. Any one size of steel, either round or square, can be used for making the tools, provided the chuck is adapted to hold them securely. It is recommended that a range of tools to suit every kind of operation likely to be dealt with should be made, and if they cannot all be contained in a hollow handle, a wooden block may be used as a holder as shown in Fig. 75.

Small silver steel tools for this purpose may be hardened by heating them to redness, and cooling them out by sticking them into a block of paraffin wax, or even an ordinary candle. This avoids brittleness and imparts just about the right temper for light work. Knitting needles contain quite a good grade of steel for this purpose, and it is surprising what can be done by very small turning tools of this type. One of their advantages is that as the area of the edge is so small, they are much less liable to dig in or " catch a crab " than larger tools. A very expert maker of chessmen used to make all his turning gouges from old steel pen nibs, ground to a suitable shape, and fitted to a holder much larger and more rigid than the ordinary penholder.

Coolant supply

The importance of a constant supply of cutting lubricant, or coolant, to lathe tools, is fully recognised in modern prac-tice, and most production lathes are fitted with a constant service by means of a pump or gravity system. The use of a pump is hardly necessary for the small quantity of coolant required in light turning operations, but something better than the common method of applying it intermittently with a brush is often desirable. A small drip-can is a very simple thing to make and fit up, but it is worth doing properly. Some makeshift arrangements are far more trouble than they are worth, and do anything but apply the coolant where it is wanted, and in the correctly regulated quantity.

Fig. 76 shows a drip-can which can be fitted to the hand-rest socket of a small lathe and thus travels with the slide rest. The spout, when once adjusted, maintains its relation to the tool point, so that the coolant is always applied at the right spot. It is only practicable to carry a small can in this way, so that in order to run for long periods without replenishing the supply, it may be better to use a fixed tank in an

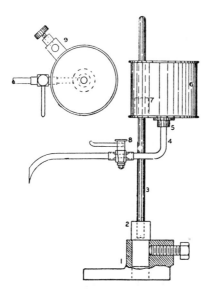

Fig. 76.—Drip-can fitted to hand-rest socket

elevated position adjacent to the lathe and connected by a flexible rubber pipe to a spout mounted on the lathe saddle, so as to be adjustable to the required position.

The drip-pipe shown in Fig. 77 is designed so that it can be instantly applied to or detached from the lathe, and to occupy the minimum space, so that it does not interfere with the manipulation of the lathe tools. As it is mounted actually on the tool post, it follows the tool point in both directions of feed.

As will be seen in the drawing, it consists of four very simple parts, A being a short length of brass or copper tube soldered to a sheet metal clip, with the flexible tube from the supply tank connected to one end of it, and the other having a short sleeve of rubber tube slipped over it to form a gland for the tube B, which should be a sliding fit inside A, and is bent and cut obliquely at the end to form a spout. The part

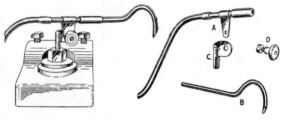

Fig. 77.—Easily-detachable drip pipe

C consists of a lug for the attachment of the clip on the part A by the pivot bolt D, and has a split plug intended to fit in a hole drilled for the purpose in the end of the tool post stud. This hole should be fitted with a pin when not in use, to prevent it being clogged up with accumulated dirt and swarf. If the drilling of such a hole is objected to, it is possible to modify the method of mounting, such as by the use of a spring clip to fit over the nut, or any other convenient projection on the tool post.

The part A may be fitted with a tap or valve to control the flow of coolant, but it is usually more convenient to do this at the supply tank, especially as it may be desired to slip the drip pipe and its flexible tube off entirely when not in use.

Slotting tools

Internal keyways in the bores of wheel bosses may be cut in the lathe by using a suitable tool applied endwise by racking the saddle backwards and forwards, while the mandrel is held stationary. A suitable tool for this purpose is shown in Fig. 78, consisting of a square shank with a turned-down end like a boring bar, but slotted horizontally across the end and fitted with a short pivoted cutter. It will be clear that this tool is automatically relieved on the return stroke by its ability to turn on the pivot to a limited extent, so that the tool point is not subjected to unnecessary friction. The height of the cutter must be exactly the same as that of the lathe centres, and this can be positively assured by making the shank of a suitable size of bar, or setting over the turned portion eccentric to it.   This device could be improved by the addition of a light spring in the slot of the bar, bearing on the heel of the cutter, so that it automatically returns to the cutting position each time after it has been withdrawn from the hole.

Another method of slotting in the lathe, in which the cutter is power-driven, is shown in the photograph, Fig. 79, which is practically self-explanatory.   It entails the use of a vertical bracket or standard mounted on the lathe bed, to which the top slide of the lathe is attached, its operating

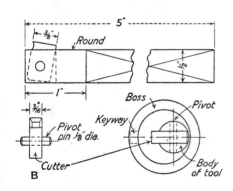

Fig. 78.—Tool for slotting internal keyways in lathe

screw being removed.   The slide is reciprocated by means of a connecting-rod from an adjustable crankpin mounted on the lathe mandrel nose or in a disc held in the chuck.   By mounting the work horizontally on the cross slide of the lathe, any form of slotting work within the capacity of the device can be done simply and quickly.

Lapping and grinding devices

When carrying out any kind of lapping or grinding in the lathe, the utmost precautions should be taken to prevent abrasive dust entering the bearings or slides. It will be found advisable to plug any open oil holes, and to cover the slides with rag or paper, oiled so that the dust will adhere to its surface and be removed without difficulty when the job is finished. Unless this care is taken, the abrasive may so work in as to be very difficult to remove, and may play havoc with accurately fitted working parts.

Fig. 79.—Power-driven slotting attachment for lathe

In the handbook *Grinding, Lapping and Honing,* several simple devices for internal and external lapping, which may be applied in any lathe, were described, together with particulars of the procedure in using them, but this book is unfortunately now out of print.

Grinding wheels are sometimes run in the lathe, but the high speeds necessary to obtain full efficiency with modern abrasives are not usually obtainable in ordinary metal working lathes ; too low a wheel speed results in very poor results, and rapid wastage of the wheel. In a general way it is better to avoid this practice, and to use a proper grinding head, however simple it may be, which can be run at the correct speed, and has no closely fitted slides to be damaged by the abrasive dust.

Lapping discs or cylinders may often be used in the lathe, as they are run at much lower speed and do not throw abrasive particles about so much as grinding wheels. The ordinary copper lap, which can be run on a mandrel or attached to the faceplate, is suitable for very fine and accurate finishing of surfaces, and its utility can be enhanced by improvising some form of work table on the cross slide of the lathe, with angular adjustment so that bevelled edges of parts, such as slide rest adjusting gibs, may be finished to close accuracy.

The so-called " laps " that are faced with emery cloth are not true laps at all, though they may be used as effective grinding wheels if run at high enough speed. Within the scope of their use in the lathe, they may be regarded as suitable for finishing purposes where accuracy is not of special importance. A wooden disc, with a sheet of emery cloth glued or cemented to its surface, may be attached to the lathe faceplate by wood screws from the back, and used in this way. Another method of attaching the emery cloth, which saves time when a disc is required immediately, is to cut a circle of it about $\frac{3}{4}$ in. larger than the diameter of the faceplate or mounting disc, and to notch the edges all round

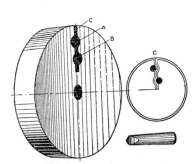

Fig. 80.—Attaching emery cloth to disc

to the depth of the overlap. The tongues thus formed are turned down and secured to the edge of the disc by binding or slipping a stout rubber band over them.

Fig. 80 shows how a strip of emery cloth can be attached to the periphery of a disc or cylinder securely and quickly. A radial slot is cut in the disc, wide enough to take two thicknesses of cloth, and holes are bored through it so as slightly to intersect the slot. The emery cloth is then passed

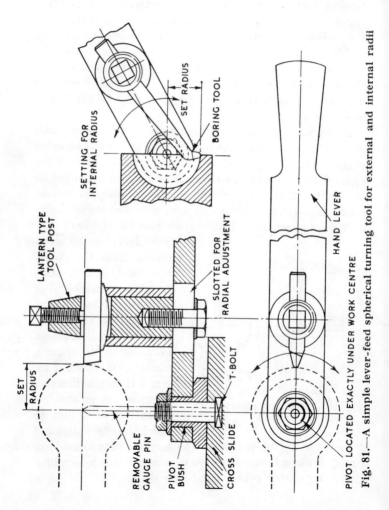

Fig. 81.—A simple lever-feed spherical turning tool for external and internal radii

around the disc and its two ends are tucked into the slot, where they are secured by two wooden pegs driven into the holes. The peg nearest the centre of the disc should be put in first, and the second one will then tighten the emery cloth so that it adheres closely all round the edge of the disc. The above methods are equally applicable to sanding discs or cylinders for finishing woodwork whether they are used in the lathe or in special sanding machines.

Ball turning tools

It is very often necessary to turn work completely or partly spherical, and even experienced turners often find it difficult to do this really accurately. If a very high degree of precision is called for, some form of generating tool, which works around a central pivot situated immediately under the axis of the work, may be found absolutely necessary. A tool of this type is shown in Fig. 81, which can be made easily, and will do most of the operations required on both internal and external spherical contours. The attachment comprises a rectangular steel bar, pivoted at one end on a shouldered bush, mounted in a fixed position on the lathe cross-slide by means of a T-bolt, and carrying a radially adjustable tool post. A convenient form of tool post, which enables the tool to be swivelled, or adjusted for height by means of a convex packing piece, is the so-called lantern or American type, and this may be attached by a set-screw on the underside, in a slot in the bar. As an alternative, the toolpost may be mounted on a small slide, with a feed screw for more delicate control of radial setting. The bar is extended to form a hand lever of any convenient length for traversing the tool in an arc around the pivot centre.

For accurate spherical machining, it is most important that the centre of the pivot should be located exactly under the centre of the workpiece in both cross and longitudinal planes. To facilitate this, the pivot bolt may be made hollow, and fitted with a removable gauge pin. For cross adjustment, the live centre is inserted in the lathe mandrel socket, and the pin lined up with it; this position of the cross-slide must be observed for the finishing cut, though the slide may be manipulated for rough machining of the work. The radial setting may be measured from the gauge pin.

To machine spherical curves internally, an ordinary boring tool may be used, but the radius is set, not by radial centre-line movement on the bar, but by swivelling the tool from the tool post centre. For this reason, the value of a tool slide is not so great as it might appear, if a good deal of internal work is to be done. The simple form of tool has been used very successfully on the external and internal parts of ball socket joints, such as that of the Universal Swivelling Vice (M.E. Plan WE.3).

In many cases very elaborate spherical generating tools, with worm feed to the tool slide, are fitted to lathes intended for this special purpose. Similar principles are applied to

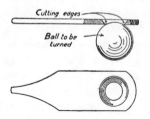

Fig. 82.—Hand tools for finishing off spherical curves

generating curved profiles which are not truly spherical, the axis of the tool slide in such cases being displaced from the centre of the work to the desired extent.

Usually, however, all that is required of parts that are turned spherically is that they should be sufficiently accurate and well finished to satisfy the eye, though even this is difficult enough by ordinary turning methods. For manufacturing purposes, a form tool would be used for these jobs, but it is often necessary to produce them in small quantities which would not justify the expense of a special tool. In such cases, the simple hand-turning tools shown in Fig. 82 will be found very useful for finishing the spherical curve, after it has been roughed out as closely as possible to its correct shape by ordinary tools. The first of these is the more suitable for use on metal work, and consists of a flat piece of tool steel swaged down to form a tang at the end, to fit a wooden handle, and having a hole drilled in it about half the diameter of the ball to be formed, bevelled off to a sharp edge at an angle of about 60 degrees. An old flat file, with the teeth ground away, and annealed to allow the hole to be drilled, then afterwards hardened and tempered, serves the purpose excellently. In use, the tool is pressed against the work, and traversed over its surface with a wobbling motion, when the edges of the hole will act as a scraper and work the surface down to a true spherical curve and a high finish. The tool can be re-sharpened by grinding the flat face.

The other tool works on the same principle, but has a much more acute cutting edge, and is therefore more suitable for soft materials such as wood, ivory, ebonite, etc. It can be made from a piece of alloy steel tube, and if fairly hard in the first place, may not need hardening and tempering. This is an advantage when the tool needs re-sharpening, as this can only be effected by machining back the internal taper in this particular case.

A tailstock drilling jig

Many lathe operators make use of a tailstock drill pad for simple drilling operations in the lathe, using a drill running in the chuck. Although this method is very handy, and saves using a drilling machine for such work, it tends to be awkward for some drilling jobs, especially for cross drilling through the diameter of a shaft. This operation can be facilitated by making a vee notch across the centre of the pad face, so as to locate the work accurately on the lathe axis, but a much wider range of usefulness is afforded by the simple device shown in Fig. 83. This consists of a drill pad which may be socketed in the tailstock in the usual way, or adapted to fit over the outside of the tailstock barrel, as shown, in which case it may be provided with a set screw for clamping it in position. Two studs are screwed into the face of the pad, and serve as guides for a cross bar, which is

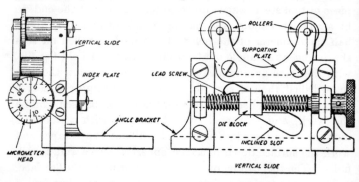

Fig. 84.—Roller filing rest, with micrometer elevating adjustment for use on engineering lathes

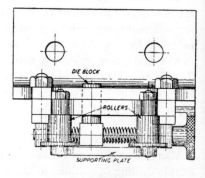

made to slide stiffly on them and is bored in the centre to take a jig bush, corresponding in bore size to the drill to be used. In order to ensure that the hole for the bush is truly central, the cross bar should be fitted to the guides and the pad

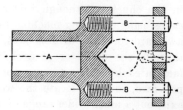

Fig. 83.—Tailstock drilling jig

set up in the lathe for drilling of this hole. It is possible to use the cross bar to clamp the work, by fitting nuts on the ends of the studs, but this is not a very good method because it tends to affect the accuracy of the studs as guides, and also eliminates the space left between the bush and the work to provide chip clearance. If the work requires clamping, it is better to make the pad large enough to take a clamp at the side of the cross bar and entirely separate from it. A set of jig bushes should be made in mild steel to fit a range of drill sizes, the entering edges being carefully rounded off and the bores smoothly and accurately finished, after which they are case-hardened.

Roller filing rest for the lathe

This is an adaptation of a device that is very popular on horological lathes, specially improved and modified so as to be useful for many operations in ordinary engineering practice. By its aid, in conjunction with a simple indexing device, squares, hexagons, etc., can be produced on turned work simply and expeditiously, without removing them from the lathe chuck, and it is also adaptable to more complex operations, such as cam forming.

Fig. 85.—Finished appearance of Fig. 84

The construction of the device is explained in Fig. 84, where it will be seen that the rollers, which are of hardened steel, are carried on pivot bolts in a bracket attached to a vertical slide. This is fitted to guides on the vertical face of a small angle bracket, so as to be capable of elevating adjustment. Movement of the vertical slide is effected in a very novel manner by means of a die block, which can be traversed horizontally, parallel to the bracket, by means of a lead screw, and engages an inclined slot in the vertical slide. The head of the screw is graduated in increments equivalent to thousandths of an inch in the vertical position of the rollers.

Fig. 86.—Roller filing rest in use

The complete appliance is shown in Fig. 85, and Fig. 86 shows it in use, for producing a hexagonal cap nut on the end of a piece of brass rod held in the lathe chuck.

Knurling tools

Many kinds of turned articles need to have serrated or " knurled " edges for the purpose of providing a hand grip, or sometimes merely for decoration. Ready-made knurling tools are generally rather expensive, especially if more than one pattern is required, but the rollers or knurls themselves can be obtained fairly cheaply and are easily mounted in suitable holders to fit the lathe tool post. A good deal of time can be saved in making the holders by building them up in three pieces from rectangular bar, held together by rivets, slightly countersunk and finished flush with the side surfaces (Fig. 87). A suitable size for the side pieces is $\frac{5}{8}$ in. by $\frac{3}{16}$ in., and the centre piece should be a little thicker than the width of the knurl to allow it to turn freely; a small amount of end play is no disadvantage. The pivot pin should be an easy fit for the knurl, but a press fit in the sides of the holder, so that it can be knocked out if required.

As the loading on the knurl is high, the pin should be made of silver steel, unhardened, or mild steel, case hardened. It should be located as close to the front top corner of the holder as consistent with strength and security, so that it will work close up to a shoulder, or near the chuck jaws.

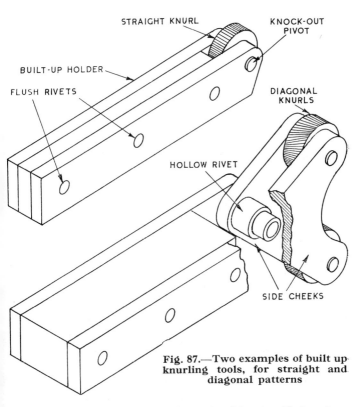

STRAIGHT KNURL

KNOCK-OUT PIVOT

BUILT-UP HOLDER

FLUSH RIVETS

DIAGONAL KNURLS

HOLLOW RIVET

SIDE CHEEKS

Fig. 87.—Two examples of built up knurling tools, for straight and diagonal patterns

Projection of the pin or rivets from the sides should therefore be avoided.

For diagonal or " diamond " knurling, it is possible to use a single knurl capable of producing the required pattern, but better results are obtainable by the simultaneous application of two spiral-cut knurls. These are held between side plates, roughly triangular in shape, joined together at the apex by a shouldered hollow rivet, which forms a bearing for the pivot pin of the main holder. In this way, swivelling movement is provided to allow the knurls to centre themselves and bear with equal pressure on the work.

As the process of knurling consists of indentation of the work surface rather than cutting, heavy side pressure on the work is necessary to carry it out properly. To eliminate this, knurling tools of more elaborate type, to apply balanced pressure on knurls located above and below the work, are recommended. They certainly reduce wear and tear of a light lathe when a considerable amount of knurling has to be done, but the simple knurling tools shown in Fig. 87 serve quite well for occasional work and do not overload the lathe mandrel if it is kept well lubricated. In the initial stages of the knurling operation, it is best to set the tool at a slight angle, to penetrate more deeply at the leading edge, and to work on only a narrow part of the surface until the proper pattern is established. Sometimes the knurls tend to " double-track," or fail to produce a pattern of the correct pitch, and it may be found necessary to " wipe out " the tracks with a lathe tool or fine file and start again, on a slightly reduced diameter. The operation should be continued with moderate pressure and ample lubrication, until the knurls penetrate to the full depth of their serrations. Incomplete knurling not only looks slovenly, but it also produces burrs which may cut the fingers when handled.

Straight knurls can be produced from silver steel bar, serrated in the lathe after turning and drilling the centre. A 60-degree point tool, with a slight radius honed on the tip, is set on its side on the toolpost, and operated by racking the saddle backwards and forwards to plane the incisions. The lathe mandrel is indexed as required to produce the specified pitch; for instance, a 60-toothed index wheel will produce incisions of approximately 0.016 in., or 1/64 in.

pitch, on a knurl of $\frac{1}{2}$ in. diameter. The knurls are finally hardened and tempered to dark straw colour. Diagonal knurls are more difficult to make, as they involve a spiral milling operation, which is beyond the scope of most small workshops.